LYNDA SNELL'S
A HERITAGE OF MBRIDGE

Her History of ARCHERS Country

CAROLE BOYD

The Archers

Virgin

To all Lyndas with a Y
(you know who you are)
this book is dedicated

Acknowledgements
I am grateful to Vanessa Whitburn, Editor of The Archers, and to Keri Davies and
Camilla Fisher for their support and advice.

My special thanks to Liz Rigbey for inventing Lynda Snell, to George Goodwin
– guide and guru – for initiating the project, to Lorna Russell and Rod Green, my
editors, for their untiring help, and to the Chief Executive of the Lynda Snell Society
for her irrepressible enthusiasm.

And to friends and family, particularly my husband, Patrick, who gave up his
study and a year of his life to enable this book to happen.

First published in 1997 by
Virgin Publishing Ltd
332 Ladbroke Grove
London W10 5AH

Picture Credits
Pages 4, 63, 86, 87, 88, 101, 103, 139 © Image Bank
Pages 6, 10, 11, 12, 15, 18, 21, 25, 26, 28, 29, 30, 38, 51, 58, 59, 68, 76, 79, 82, 95, 118 © Chris Brown
Pages 16, 19, 20, 22, 32, 40, 41, 50, 53, 60, 61, 71, 74, 100, 110, 130, 133, 134, 135 © Hulton Getty
Pages 8, 23, 34, 43, 44, 45, 47, 48, 55, 84, 87, 113, 114, 120, 125, 127, 137, 141 © BBC
Pages 22, 36, 37, 41, 42, 56, 62, 64, 65, 66, 69, 75, 78, 79, 80, 81, 91, 93, 99, 107, 129, 131 © Mary Evans Picture Library
Pages 104, 105, 117 © Private Collection
Pages 109, 119 © Archers Addicts
Pages 142 -159 © Christine Hart-Davies

A catalogue record for this book is available from the British Library.

ISBN 185227 658 4

Designed by Blackjacks Limited
Reproduction by Scanners
Printed in Italy

Contents

Prologue

*H*ello! and welcome to my version of all things rustic and rural. For some time now, I've been ruminating, in a Keatsian way, on the simple beauty of the countryside. How lucky we are to live in this land which is still 'green and pleasant', despite the ravages of developers and entrepreneurs, and yes, in some cases, farmers.

Of course, much has been written on the subject over the years, and I would never dream of challenging immortals like Wordsworth et al., but I know from my postbag that I am not alone (although it sometimes seems so), and I feel the time has come to catalogue my thoughts for posterity.

It is now ten years since Robert and I arrived in Ambridge from leafy Sunningdale. 'Only ten years?' I hear you cry. 'It seems so much longer!' But the time has flown by, crowded with excitement, good times and bad, happiness and heartache – and always with our mission to 'give', in a Green way, to the local inhabitants.

Of course, there have been occasions when certain of those inhabitants harangued one with the question, 'Whaddya wanna leave Sunningdale for, Missis? Eh? Tell me that?' And, yes, why on earth would Robert and I wish to leave a highly desirable oasis of privilege, surrounded by all the right scenery and most of the 'right' people, with a full social life and low-stress drive away from Bracknell's Silicon Valley for Robert.

The answer is simple – Doreen Purefoy! I am well aware that Ambridge has had its share of bossy, interfering, social-climbing females – they know who they are – but they pale into insignificance beside the overwhelming impertinence of that woman. Thankfully, by coming out of denial and owning the fact that there was no room for both of us, and that I was never going to 'arrive' in Sunningdale while she was around, I 'escaped' from a semi-suburban Green Belt of pretension and privilege to the truly rural, grass-roots environment of Ambridge, where simple values count and one can really call a pig a pig!

For the visitor to Ambridge and Borsetshire who seeks to know more than the usual guidebook can afford, I intend to reveal what lies between the lines, under the carpets and down the backs of the sofas, as it were, of the customs, history, folklore, wildlife and social mores of this delightful area of England.

A Village Walkabout

I am always intrigued to discover that most visitors to Grey Gables see me as the fount of all local knowledge, while most *locals* seem to consider that it is Jennifer Aldridge who holds that title. I put it down to the years of conditioning these same villagers had to endure prior to my arrival in Ambridge, plus their reluctance to look more ... imaginatively at their surroundings.

But the fact remains that I have a pivotal position on Reception – I am the first human being the visitors set eyes on after leaving their car and crossing the threshold. (Unless they are unlucky enough to be accosted by Higgs in portering mode when there is always the danger that they might never make it up the steps.)

Anyway, assuming they do, they are rewarded by my well-groomed presence and warm, knowing (in the sense of informed, that is) smile, as they approach my desk. So I don't think it's an exaggeration to say that I am, indeed, one of the sights of Ambridge.

Certainly, it is in that first moment of bonding that guests realise that they can trust me to enhance their visit by advising them to explore those parts of Ambridge which other sources of information may not have reached (NB J. Aldridge *et al*!).

I always make a point of basing my recommendations on tried and tested personal experiences – it *is* the only way – but I am sorry to say that this has led to the occasional ... misunderstanding. Take the case of the travelling salesman who thought that my innocent arrangement to meet him one evening in Felpersham, to show him the cathedral, meant – well, something quite different! (Robert was very understanding about the whole sordid business and was able to reassure me that my general demeanour and appearance couldn't possibly have encouraged such a degrading misinterpretation.)

Grey Gables offers four-star accommodation, and, thanks to me, all visitors receive a warm welcome to Ambridge.

7

But, by and large, I think guests are quite entertained by my little tutorials on the history of Ambridge as they stand waiting to check in, tired and travel-stained and surrounded by luggage.

The only problem is that they often seem so energised by my commentary that they rush off when I'm only halfway through, eager to get to the nearest interesting sight asap. Caroline once hinted that maybe they were eager to get to a hot bath and a stiff drink to recover – from the journey I assumed, but she merely smiled and moved discreetly away. I'm very fond of Caroline, but I do think she misses the point sometimes.

However, I digress – in fact, I plan to explore the Art of Digression throughout this book (as you will have realised by now), since I feel that some of one's most inspired work is often surrounded by brackets, dots and dashes. So do look out for these – maybe younger visitors might like to keep score – I believe they add a weight and texture to one's style, akin to that of Dickens, Trollope and Georgette Heyer.

To continue – much has been written about the significant history and architecture of the area and, frankly, I don't intend to repeat any of it – not to a living soul! If I can possibly help it.

Instead, let me take you on a leisurely stroll – post hot bath and stiff G&T – to peek behind the scenes, as it were, of this delightful Victorian-Gothic country house hotel.

You will already have sampled the delights of your en suite bathroom and mini-bar, gazed out across the country park from your mullioned window,

Caroline and Jean-Paul having a bilingual conversation on matters culinary.

and glanced at the enticing menu, in anticipation of dinner later on. But, may I suggest that you refrain from ordering prawn cocktail – yes, I know it's on the menu! Suffice it to say that our (genuine) French chef, Jean-Paul, has an irrational fear of this dish, and has been known to throw a *crise de nerfs* at its mere mention. I have advised Mr Woolley, the owner, to withdraw it from the menu, but he refuses, point blank, saying it reminds him of the good old days in Stirchley, before he became a sophisticate! You should, however, be quite safe with crevettes or langoustines – served naked, as Nature intended.

Passing the Ballroom, with its magnificent chandelier, cleaned errati-cally by Higgs on a biennial basis, you may glimpse the elegant terrace, and yet more evidence of Higgs in the pots, urns and borders, ablaze with his horticultural genius – he is devoted to every form of chrysanthemum known to Man. Higgs pops up all over the place, a man of many parts – none of them speaking. But you will always be able to identify him by his trousers, which remain steadfastly horticultural, no matter whether he is playing porter, chauf-feur/devotee of Mr Woolley's Bentley, pool attendant (in the Health Club), golf caddie (bookable at the club house), boot boy, page or general factotum.

I have complained about Higgs's trousers, of course, and the debilitating effect they have on staff and guests alike, despite Caroline's assertion that visiting gentry emulate them. In fact, I cited them as an example of the need for changes and improvements in my Business Plan presentation to Mr Woolley and Caroline, when I interviewed for the post of assistant manager. I also outlined my strategy for sharpening up other staff members, like Trudy and Shelley, on the matter of decorum in the kitchen. And I can quite see that by making Trudy the new assistant manager they have, in a way, utilised the psychology of encouraging by responsibility. But to find oneself still on Reception, though in a permanent way, was a defining moment for me, and one which Robert was astute enough to quantify positively:

'Lyndy, it's quite obvious they realise that someone with your social skills would be wasted in an admin. job. They *need* you on Reception, in the public eye, interacting with guests, welcoming, organising and informing. Anyway, you're the only one who can work the computer.'

I returned to my post the next day with new *éclat*, informing Mr Woolley that Trudy would have my unconditional support, particularly if she remem-bered my helpful tips on poise and deportment. I think he was hoping that I might even become Trudy's role model – well, one is happy to give, as always, but only time will tell if Trudy is quite ready to receive one's largesse as graciously as one would wish.

Thankfully, the threat of increased career demands distracting me from all my projects and campaigns has been averted, and I still have time and energy to continue as before. So what could have been a burden has become a blessing, which is not to say I shan't be watching Trudy like a hawk for signs of slipshod attitude or falling standards – I owe it to Mr Woolley to maintain my role as Caring Caretaker in Residence.

I suggest you reconnoitre the Health Club for later in your schedule. It has everything a fitness freak could possibly require and I do recommend the Health Food Bar, if only for the Bridge Farm organic yoghurt – try pistachio for a green mood. Health Club membership is available for an annual fee of around £400, but visitors merit a special inclusive rate: tariff available at Reception.

You could well be ready to meander down the drive from Grey Gables, towards the Lodge. This is an attractive black and white timbered building, typical of the estate lodges one might see from a passing car and think, 'How charming! I wonder what it's like inside.'

Well, may I suggest that you make this your chance to find out.

The Lodge is the home of Jack and Peggy Woolley and, before I go any further, I feel there are a couple of very interesting things you need to know about Peggy: (a) her first husband, Jack, was a humble publican, landlord of the Bull to be precise; (b) her second husband, also Jack curiously enough (and this could explain much), is a very rich and successful businessman/owner of Grey Gables (i.e. she is the boss's wife).

I shan't say more than that – I prefer to keep it as a nuance of village life, but I'm afraid I'm always slightly suspicious of people who marry for money. Of course, I've got nothing against Peggy, and she's good to her family, but I think it would be true to say that we have only two things in common: eggs and bathrooms.

I refer, of course, to (1) her absurd *over*-sensitivity concerning my *Keep*

The Lodge — very black and white isn't it.

Ambridge Tidy video some years ago. No, I'm sorry, but she dropped those eggs, in public, outside the village shop, in full view of everyone, and in my book that counts as litter-bugging; (2) her total *lack* of sensitivity in demoting me from receptionist to chambermaid last year in Caroline's absence at home on post-honeymoon leave. I could see that even Mr Woolley was secretly shocked, but he relapsed into one of his occasional attacks of spinelessness. (If he were the heroic type I might call this his tragic flaw, in a Bardian context, but as it is…) The sympathetic vibes may have been there but – sorry – too late!

One thing I *do* know, and that is that I shall think of Peggy Woolley every time I clean the bathroom at Ambridge Hall. It will *not* be with affection, though the energy thus generated will certainly enable me to get the job done in double quick time.

Thankfully, I think I'm a big enough person not to let injured feelings play any part in what I'm about to suggest to the innocent visitor to Ambridge, hell-bent on heritage.

Why not casually call on the Woolleys *en passant*, as it were? Tell them you're staying at Grey Gables and how you've always wanted to see inside a 'real' lodge. Mention you hear that this is the love nest they created on their marriage, that you can't wait to see the stained glass window in the hall and the delightful collection of china, not to mention the flower-filled conservatory and the electronic cat-flap.

It's hard to miss this statue of Aphrodite in Jack and Peggy's garden.

Insist on a tour of the garden and admire its design (one of mine, actually; they won me in a raffle). You could make few apt comments on the statue, a gift from him to her and, as you might imagine, the cause of early marital discord. Run the soil through your fingers to check its friability, making sure that it sticks to your shoes and gets well-ingrained under your finger nails and then, just when Peggy thinks she's getting rid of you, ask if you may use the bathroom. Once inside, think of me – and do your worst!

Then, ignoring the distant sounds of annoyance bordering on rage coming from the Lodge, bear left towards the village. You are now passing in the shadow of Lakey Hill, a famous local landmark rising to 771 feet (I'm afraid the metric system is *still* 'under consideration' in Ambridge).

One wouldn't call Lakey Hill majestic exactly – I mean, it's not the Alps, or even a

Lakey Hill: a natural beauty spot steeped in local history and lore of every kind.

Langdale Pike – but here, on the edge of the Cotswolds or whatever, it counts as impressive, especially when you know what's been going on underneath it all these years.

I like to think of it as a gracious, scenic backdrop to the village, sheltering, but never threatening. But, 'twas not ever thus! For beneath that smooth, balding summit, denuded of vegetation by countless bonfires celebrating anything from the non-invasion of Napoleon to VE Day and the Silver Jubilee and scarred by occasional invasions of bikers burning rubber in what remains of the gorse and bracken, there lie the remains of a prehistoric burial ground.

Pause, passer-by, to dwell on the rites of passage of those early Ambridge folk who once inhabited this mystic place:

The lordly ones,
Who dwell in the hills,
In the hollow hills.

Yes, it does require a feat of imagination to relate some of today's inhabitants to those dignified primitives, though I suppose they couldn't all have been dignified, and certainly not all the time. Perhaps only when performing ceremonial interments.

No, mostly, they would be hanging out in their equivalent of the Bull – a filthy, damp cave, huddled round a bleak fire to form a sort of early 'snug', exchanging rudimentary language on the subject of whose turn it was to kill the next dinosaur, or organise a campaign to rid the area of wolves. The more sensitive ones might be running art classes on the cave walls, providing a little culture for future generations to appreciate, but they would be in a minority; hunting and cooking, eating and drinking, sleeping and – that sort of thing – would be the pattern.

Maybe a case of *plus ça change, plus c'est la même chose* after all!

Anyway, all that's visible of this piece of our heritage today are a few bumps and hollows which, so Kathy Perks informed me, were mistaken for an overgrown golf course by Al and Mary-Jo Clancy when they stayed at Ambridge Hall last year.

I'm sorry, but I refuse to believe it! I've often noticed that Kathy has a tendency to the whimsical, which is something she needs to monitor. I may only have met the Clancys briefly, and yes, they were certainly quite … intense, but they did live in my house for two whole weeks, and one has to remember they *are American!* Moreover, they were such keen golfers that they could well have hallucinated at the mere thought of a golf course.

Thank goodness for Bert Fry who, graciously accepting my offer of a half of Shires, helped me to get the whole thing into perspective by agreeing with me, wise countryman that he is. He also came up with some very interesting information.

It seems that what is not so well-chronicled is the fact that Lakey Hill was once thought to be part of the estate of Sir Lancelot of the Lake, or Sir Lancelot du Lac, or even Sir Lancelot du Lakey Hill, as he preferred to be addressed.

Apparently, it was granted to him by King Arthur in recognition of his prowess against Sir Gawain the Green Knight, Sir Mordred *et al.*, and long before his unfortunate affair with Queen Guinevere.

I must say, I like Tennyson's resplendent picture of him riding between the barley sheaves on the Am side of Willow Farm, singing, 'Tirra, lirra, by the river' – probably a fragment from a passing troubadour's ditty.

Bert, who not only writes but, secretly, also reads poetry, is convinced that Sir Lancelot was en route to a clandestine tryst with Queen Guinevere (who had sought sanctuary with Blessed Brenda of Borchester in the monastery near Home Farm) when he was glimpsed by the Lady of Shalott.

'It were terrible, Missis. There she were, 'oled up on this island in the middle of the Am, and he come by, and we all know what that led to!'

I was tempted to test Bert's knowledge of English literature by asking exactly what it *did* lead to, but I was so charmed by his quaint confusion of truth and fiction that I refrained, aware of the importance of letting his imagination go with his creative flow!

Nevertheless, the most likely outcome to the whole tragic business is that, when the crunch finally came for Lancelot and Guinevere, Blessed Brenda was defrocked for harbouring an unruly royal and headed for Waterley Cross, to set up as the first of a long line of witches. And, no doubt, she would have been joined by the Lady of Shalott had not her unfortunate crush on Sir L led to her tragic and watery demise.

There are always those who like to trivialise and I will not name the person who said that Lakey Hill is the perfect spot from which to spy on one's neighbours – you know who you are! I choose to regard it in a more noble light, as a beauty spot which reflects the tranquillity of a still relatively unspoilt landscape. Below you spread fields and farms and Ambridge itself, unviolated by a feeder road (thanks to a campaign of mine), and, yes, it *is* possible to make out young Daniel Hebden feeding the ducks on the village pond, or Pat Archer leaving the shop with several tins of mixed veg. in her basket (obviously a panic on in the organic farm kitchen!).

I think the Bard gets it right yet again (and he must have had a Bert Fry in mind) when he wrote in *Henry VI Part III*:

> *O God, methinks it were a happy life*
> *To be no better than a homely swain;*
> *To sit upon a hill, as I do now …*

By the way, it has come to my attention that Joe Grundy, in his so-called ode, 'The Hob Hound', has had the audacity to refer to Lakey Hill as Mount Ararat. Let me say, here and now, that this is yet another example of confusing truth with fiction and is the product of an over-fertile imagination, possibly induced by inhaling slurry fumes at muck spreading time.

To continue village-wards, you will see a turning to your right, but don't bother to take it unless you are a rich philanthropist, or a property developer with a good credit rating, because Arkwright Hall is a dilapidated seven-teenth-century mansion needing total refurbishment, and even the attention of the pest control officer I should think.

Some have tried and failed – even the discovery of a priest-hole didn't help – but, though it may have a rather unattractive exterior, a little TLC could work wonders for Arkwright Hall (and for a few people I can think of, too!). In fact, I'm seriously thinking of adding it to my list of future campaigns, perhaps under the working title 'Arkwright Hall – Get a Life!' I shall give the matter some thought.

By now, you should have reached Ambridge proper, unless of course you've wandered off left, down to The Green council housing development (well, every village must have one, I suppose). I don't have anything against The Green, but it is fairly unremarkable, apart, that is, from Susan Carter's neo-Georgian front door, which still sticks out like a sore thumb and continues to jeopardise our chances in the Best Kept Village competition, despite my warnings.

I say Susan's because I don't think Neil had much to do with it; in fact I just don't think his heart was in it at all. Well, Betty intimated as much when I broached the subject in the shop one day; she went on to reveal that they had also invested in carpet tiles! I must say, I thought that was the last straw. I mean, it's not as though Neil has money to throw around, especially since they now have a mortgage on the house and, if only Susan had come to me,

I reluctantly draw your attention to Susan Carter's front door. See what I mean?

I could have designed a scheme for her which would definitely have avoided using the above items.

Now that I think about it, I'm rather hurt, because I know that Susan regards me as something of a role-model – ever since the day I offered her a glass of sherry. And of course, I'm not talking polished oak floorboards and Chinese rugs *à la* mode d'Ambridge Hall – heavens no! That would be inappropriate for the children and, let's face it, unlikely to be really appreciated by parents who are still struggling to belong to the aspirational classes.

But, looking on the bright side, the floor covering and general decor of Number 1, The Green may be the victim of mere hearsay so, to put the record straight, why not knock on the door and ask to look around at what you've heard is an imaginative approach to making the most of council property which is, despite everything, semi-detached.

So, heading back, you will see the village hall on your right, formerly the village school. Yes, it was on this spot that the likes of Bert Fry, Walter Gabriel and Joe Grundy learnt the three Rs, in the days when such things still existed.

Even Eddie Grundy must have learnt *something* here, though one wonders from whom, if his post-educative behaviour is anything to go by. I'm tempted to wonder if Eddie's translation of the Latin *educare* (to lead out) was behind the story of the time he led all his fellow pupils out of the classroom one morning claiming that, 'as the innocent victims of an oppressive capitalist regime', they were now 'on strike for a three-day school week'. All twenty-five of them were later discovered scrumping apples which, it was believed, ended up in Grundy's Special Brew Cider – and are we surprised?!

It is sad, but true, that by 1973, many parents were sending their children to schools outside Ambridge, so it was decided to close the school rather than try to raise money for repairs. But there are those villagers who still manage to raise a smile at the memory of the young Eddie's alleged

Ambridge Village School pre-Eddie Grundy.

escapades – the initials EG, not necessarily his, carved into every desk and blackboard in the place, or the series of unexplained shoebag fires which blackened the name tags of every peg in the cloakroom. They are more likely to raise an eyebrow at the recollection of the extra-mural activities behind the bike shed that caused people at the time to say, 'I 'ear that Eddie Grundy's been up to his tricks again. No good will come o' that lad, not with 'is genes!'

On the plus side, it was fire insurance money which finally created today's village hall and its vital role in bringing the community together.

For me personally, the village hall represents the home of village entertainment, the focus for all thespian endeavour, which I think I can say, without prejudice, has positively burgeoned in my time. So much so that when I replaced Clarrie as guest speaker in the village hall, my talk entitled 'Drama in the community' had the entire WI completely mesmerised, especially as they were expecting 'From bud to bloom in the greenhouse'.

Yes, the village hall has earned its reputation as a worthy home of the Arts. But if you're of a less sensitive persuasion, you could always attend the bring-and-buys, WI lectures and sponsored pancake tossing activities (the ceiling still bears witness) on offer to the refreshingly uncomplicated among our community.

As by now you will be ready for the legendary half of Shires, your next stop will have to be the Bull, and it is here that you're most likely to hear the time-honoured local greeting, 'And what brings you 'ere?'

This form of address is *de rigueur* in these parts and is used by absolutely everybody to everybody else at every possible opportunity. Unless, of course, as in your case, you happen to be passing through, or, as in my case, you are still considered to be a newcomer after ten tears! At least, that's the only reason I can think of. But the fact remains that *nobody* has *ever* said 'And what brings you 'ere, Mrs Snell?' to me, and yet they're always saying it to each other.

I did try saying it myself, to Mike Tucker actually (not a good choice, I admit). He just looked blank and said, 'I'm delivering the milk, whaddus it look like?' Just what one might expect from Mike, who I often feel is wasted in the country – he'd make such a good trade union leader, always disagreeing with the right people while upholding his right to practise free enterprise himself.

I tried it out another time on William Grundy as he came speeding up the drive on his new bike, a gift from Caroline Pemberton, his godmother:

'Hello William, and what brings you here?'

'Erm – can yer lend us a fiver, Missis Snell?'

'No, William, I never *lend* money, but I'll *give* you a fiver!'

Any tour of Ambridge would be incomplete without a stop at the Bull.

'Oh, Great! Pound coins'll do...'

'...If you do something to earn it, William'

'Oh, er – what?'

'Well, something that needs doing urgently would be good – '

'Oh, I know, I'll paint your old butcher's bike – it's an 'orrible colour!'

'Yes, alright, alright, William ...'

There followed an abortive attempt by William to extract money from me in exchange for painting my trusty bike a different colour. He seems to have forgotten the time I actually gave him my bike to cheer him up after losing his own in the Grange Farm fire. Well, I haven't! Nor have I forgotten how he gave it back in favour of Caroline's gift of a brand new model; nor shall I easily forget his remarks about its colour and vintage.

So, I'm afraid he left empty-handed and my bike remains its glorious yellow to this day. But I still don't know the truth about 'What brought him there'!

However, back to the Bull. Assuming the place hasn't suddenly gone quiet at the sight of a stranger – (I never believe that people behave like that outside a Western saloon or a TV commercial, do you? And though it's unlikely that they would in the Bull, for fear of missing out on a bit of gossip, you could find that Eddie or Joe Grundy might be silently sizing you up, ready to slither into a conversation over a free drink, so be warned!) – you should, by now, be ordering a half of Shires in the Ploughman's Bar.

You might be served by Sid Perks, the landlord, or Kathy, his wife, whose job at Grey Gables I almost inherited, indeed *should* have inherited, but for some misplaced loyalty by Mr Woolley and Caroline towards Trudy. But I've got over it all now, having proved my worth as the key person 'front of house'.

On the other hand, you might just as easily be served by Clarrie Grundy, Susan Carter or Betty Tucker – they're all dab hands at being peripatetic when needs must, which is most of the time. (And I admire them for it – bar work is something I could never entertain with my qualifications, though hostessing, of the right kind, is a possibility.) I've never quite managed to work out the staffing system at the Bull, or even if there is one, and I don't suppose Sid would know, or even believe in such things. But he's a dear fellow and manages to be all things to all men in the nicest possible way – he's always very polite to me anyway – and he will make you welcome in a delightfully unassuming way.

The Bull is a rather attractive fifteenth-century black and white inn, complete with ghost and Morris Men up to their tricks on May Day.

The Bull sign had actually come loose when Robert and I arrived in Ambridge in 1986 (heavens, how time flies!) and in the time it took for Sid to have a new one made Robert had said he couldn't possibly drink in a pub with a wonky sign – 'it is not what I've come to the country for!' I must explain that we were still very new to village life and I hadn't quite eradicated the latent yuppie in Robert, but I wasn't prepared for him to decamp for a pint at the Cat and Fiddle.

Well, I could have told him, and did so when he returned much later, looking rather pink and dishevelled and mumbling that the place was full of 'alternative people', which is Robert's gentle PC way of saying they were all either 'too young' or 'too scruffy', adjectives which, to my mind, merely scratch the surface of the goings-on at the Cat and Fiddle.

Morris Men seem incapable of keeping their feet on the ground!

At least Sid is pretty hot on under-age drinking at the Bull, though less vigilant on the sartorial aspect of some of his clientele. I don't think it's asking too much of the likes of Joe Grundy to put on a tie when cadging drinks in the Ploughman's; after all, I'm sure he would if he were in church, or in his case chapel, and since drinking is almost like a religion to him, I can't see the problem. Perhaps that's why he tends to stay in the public bar with the open fire, the darts and the dominoes.

If you decide to lunch at the Bull, may I suggest you avoid Freda's meat pies. Freda is Bert Fry's wife, a delightful soul and a wizard with a glut of strawberries and a Kilner jar. However, popular though her meat pies are with the undiscriminating, the ingredients sometimes show a little more imagination than the sensitive palate could wish for, possibly due to her husband's influence. Personally, I find the Brie and grape baguette is a safer bet.

You should be safe from the fruit machine, which apparently held Tom Forrest in its thrall some years ago, but you might get a glimpse of the peacocks wandering about in the garden – please don't upset them by calling them 'ducks', as young Jamie Perks is wont to do, because the noise they make carries all

Peacock showing off as usual.

the way to the Hall and reminds one of the more eccentric examples of *musique concrète*. Even the sound of rutting deer at Home Farm pales into the realms of 'In a Monastery Garden' by comparison.

If you happen to be a water diviner, you'll be intrigued to know that in the great rains of 1982 the waters of the Am rose and flooded the Bull's cellars – I know, it seems incredible, doesn't it? But inevitably, it led to *some* people demanding a reduction on 'flood-damaged' Shires, claiming that the water had penetrated the casks and diluted the contents. It is also said that, in that same year, Lyttlelton Bridge was blocked by piles of logs floating down from Bridge Farm.

Question: Could the Grundys have exploited the ravages of Mother Nature and deliberately actioned a log jam to divert the water towards the Bull, just so that they could get cheap beer?

Answer: Yes – I wouldn't put anything past them, and I hope that Sid wouldn't either after that sort of skulduggery. Fortunately, Borchester Fire Brigade offered Sid a very good deal on the beer after they'd pumped out the cellar, so honour was satisfied and the Grundys retired, bruised, from the fray.

As you leave the Bull, and I'm assuming that you're not having problems walking or focussing, you can just glimpse Honeysuckle Cottage across the village green and past the duckpond. This charming thatched cottage was the home of Walter Gabriel – a legend in his own lifetime – and a true old-style rustic, full of fun and folklore, and much-loved to this day.

His son Nelson still lives there, but I don't recommend you to knock on his door: he suffers from a very dry sense of humour and one isn't always sure how to take him. His reputation in the world of antiques is unparalleled, if sometimes unreliable, though I have had occasion to speak severely to him about his valuations of one or two little items at the Hall. I remember he was very unimaginative about my *escritoire* which has always been universally

*Honeysuckle Cottage –
Nelson Gabriel lives here.*

admired, even by Marjorie Antrobus who seems to think she has the monopoly on unusual pieces. (I've often observed that her display of Kikuyu worry beads is very attractive, but hardly 'in' as a collectable at the moment – but she won't listen!)

Still, Nelson has a knack of redeeming himself by offering one a chic little Chablis at his wine bar in Borchester, so one can never be cross with him for long.

But I would advise you to study this fine example of the English thatcher's craft – one that still survives, thankfully – but don't gawp, and *don't* stand at the gable end of the cottage any longer than necessary: it once collapsed in the night and frightened Nelson witless (possibly because it was also the notorious 'Night of the Black Satin Sheets' – No, I'm not at liberty to elaborate!). Although it was restored, I'm not too sure who the builder was. If it was Jason you *might* be safe, and I've every confidence in Sean, even though he doubles as landlord of the Cat and Fiddle. However, Sean wasn't around in those days, so perhaps you'd better do your studying of the thatcher's craft from the safety of the village green.

Crossing the green, take a stroll round the pond, maybe throwing any adhering crumbs of Brie and grape baguette to the ducks (they'll eat anything) and contemplate the tradition inherent in this spot. Every typical

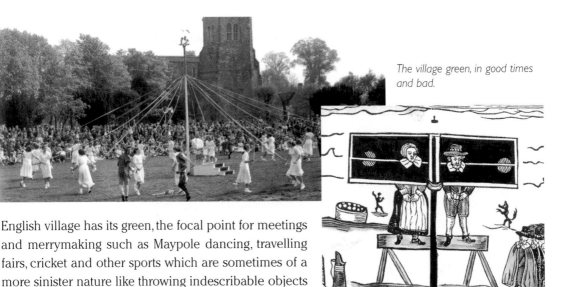

The village green, in good times and bad.

English village has its green, the focal point for meetings and merrymaking such as Maypole dancing, travelling fairs, cricket and other sports which are sometimes of a more sinister nature like throwing indescribable objects at prisoners in the stocks, and even witch ducking.

It's also true that the pond has doubled as an unofficial rubbish dump over the years, but of course, no-one would ever admit it.

Indeed, it was because of this disturbing fact that during one of my early campaigns I decided to wade into the pond and take a much-needed water sample. To my horror, but not to my surprise, biological analysis proved the said sample to be ecologically *dead*.

The pressure was on, because the Best Kept Village competition was fast approaching and, if we were to have a fighting chance, my objective of cleaning up this blot on the landscape was of the utmost priority. Well, try telling *that* to a crowd of apathetic villagers! Some people did their bit, of course – I seem to remember Jill Archer and Bert Fry being prevailed upon to lend a hand.

By now, you will have seen enough of Ambridge to want to send a post-card home, so cross over to the village shop/post office, where Betty Tucker will provide a limited, but quite impressive, range of cards – you might even unearth a faded, but picturesque, postcard of Honeysuckle Cottage – and an extensive, but unimpressive, range of everything else. I blame Jack Woolley, the owner (I did say he was an entrepreneur), for this quite unnecessary state of affairs – Betty is perfectly capable of kicking over the traces, and thinking creatively, given her head.

However, you will soon realise, as you rifle through browsers full of processed peas and sliced white bread in a hopeless quest for fresh root ginger or oyster sauce, that you are now at the nerve centre of village gossip – the Bull has got nothing on the shop!

Some say that this is because the shop is where the female population traditionally tend to hang out. True of course, up to a point, because who else can be trusted to do the nurturing and nourishing in most communities. I certainly wouldn't let Robert loose in the shop, unless I was prepared to eat a diet of crisps, peanuts, chocolate digestive biscuits, fish fingers, tinned spaghetti hoops and Frosties with Carnation milk. Thankfully, I've just about cured him of that sort of behaviour, though I'm under no illusion about what can still happen when I'm away from home on one of my courses, judging from the sweet wrappers I find in the car ashtray from time to time!

But, take it from me, any rumours supposedly coined in the merely male environs of the Bull will undoubtedly have originated in the shop, especially in dear Martha's day. Enlightened as she was in so many ways, Martha saw herself in the role of Guru, passing on her superior knowledge to her

Bridge Farm shop sells organic produce. (Maybe wear your gardening gloves when selecting vegetables.)

disciples over a packet of Gypsy creams or a bottle of bleach (the intransigently un-Green are always with us, I fear – but one must never give up!).

Betty, of course, is much more discreet and prefers the role of enabler, hearing all but saying little, and no, I don't think that's infuriating at all; I think it's really rather sensible, in the circumstances. But then, that's Betty – supportive, non-judgmental and hardworking. She can ask me for a reference any time! I have very happy memories of her time 'helping' me in our early days at the Hall, and I think it was probably watching Betty ruining her hands scrubbing the tiles in the conservatory and beeswaxing the oak refectory table in the dining room that encouraged me to stick it out during my chambermaid period at Grey Gables – I owe her a great deal.

Leaving the shop, and trying to ignore the ever-intrusive jangle of the doorbell (how does Betty put up with it? I would have spoken to Jack Woolley long ago if I were in her shoes), you will pass a somewhat insignificant property – the former village bakery in the days of Doughy Hood. I never knew Doughy, but it must have been wonderful to wake up to the smell of his fresh-baked bread every morning, and to pop down to the bakery, basket on arm, to collect a crusty cottage loaf wrapped in a red spotted handkerchief, or even a French-style baguette (though perhaps that might have been asking too much in those pre-EC days).

It goes without saying, that Bert Fry claims that Doughy Hood was a direct descendant of – you've guessed it – Robin, having come down from the East Midlands many years ago! Well, I'm simply not prepared to argue with Bert, but I think it's more likely that he was actually a descendant of the Miller in Chaucer's *Canterbury Tales* and that he adopted the name Hood as a token of respectability, in order to offset the unsavoury associations of his true lineage.

I did try to illustrate this theory to Bert by reading him an extract from *The Miller's Tale* – in the original Middle English, of course. It was about as effective, in terms of communication, as the time Robert and I were vacationing in Kansas and I faxed Bert urgently about the village panto – that is, 'Message not received'.

You might like to make a left down towards Christine Barford's stables. I'm not a horse person myself, as I discovered when she gave me a lesson in the early days, but you might fancy a hack later on – she's very good, especially with absolute beginners.

Sadly, there are always those who are destined never to progress beyond that stage, and yes, I admit it, I am one of the equine-disadvantaged when it comes to horses. I still haven't sourced the problem, but I always get the feeling that the horse knows something I don't. It's very unnerving, and frankly not something I'm prepared to put up with, even from a dumb animal.

Much fairer all round, and more dignified too I feel, to turn up at the occasional point-to-point, walk the course, hands deep in Barbour pockets (having discreetly applied the lipsalve) and picnic in the lee of the Land-Rover (casually checking out the standard of neighbouring picnics and thankful to have insisted on packing the champagne flutes rather than Robert's ghastly, but practical, plastic beakers).

I always find that the social intercourse – hopefully leading to invitations to cocktails or dinner with the right sort of person – on these occasions more than compensates for the unpleasantness of windburn or pushy Thelwell children or trying to train one's field glasses on a moving object in a force four gale with streaming eyes! (Diary dates of local point-to-points available on request from Reception.)

Head onwards towards Brookfield Farm, the Archer family's lovely old brick and timber farmhouse, dating back to the fifteenth century and set in one of Ambridge's four mediaeval open fields with a period hedge to prove it!

Brookfield Farm – equally black and white.

Generations of Archers have lived here, Dan and Doris being the most celebrated in living memory, and now Phil and Jill. And I must say that, by and large, they are proof that being a farmer doesn't necessarily mean you're not a nice person. Not that Jill Archer hasn't had her moments, and challenging me in public over my Ambridge video was one of them, though I have long since decided to overlook the incident.

Phil, of course, manages to display quite a degree of integrity (for a farmer, that is) and what with his musical skills, erratic though they sometimes may be, and his culinary escapades in the farm kitchen, he is developing into quite a rounded person.

David and Ruth Archer live nearby in The Bungalow – that much-maligned word, so redolent of 1920s suburbia (largely thanks to the observations of J. Betjeman, if you ask me) and quite inappropriate for a rural ambiance like Brookfield. Especially when one recalls that it was those British ex-pats returning from the gracious life-style of the colonies who brought the word with them. One can only assume that back in England, where it was becoming increasingly difficult to 'get the staff', the bungalow became somehow synonymous with an implied fall from power, having to get by, settling for a scratch meal of mutton stew and cabinet pudding, instead of an elegant dinner party, with silver service and brandy and cigars in the library.

An artist's impression of Home Farm – minus disfiguring silo (if only).

Well, I don't wish to cast aspersions on a hard-working wife, mother and farmer like Ruth, but she does have a reputation for living on takeaways and leaving a pile of ironing to air itself, so perhaps she and David have indirectly and unwittingly updated the bungalow's image to the nineties and I don't need to apologise for them after all – *what* a relief!

You should now take the short cut along the field path to the bridge over the Am towards Ambridge Hall, but may I suggest that you don't call in – not just yet, anyway. Much better to save yourself for it!

Instead bear right then left to Home Farm, the Aldridge residence and largest farm in Ambridge. This early eighteenth-century house was once known as Ambridge Court, built on the foundations of the ancient Lyttleton Manor. You will have observed that an essential peculiarity of Ambridge architecture is that, to ensure a building will retain its vintage value, it should always be built on top of something even older. I can see the heritage concept at work here, but I can't help sharing the cynic's view that a cowboy builder would be only too eager to add it to his list of useful excuses/explanations for crumbling walls and 'dodgy foundations, luv!' And frankly, I am thankful that the Hall is sitting happily on its very own, solid, Victorian foundations and has no need of further flimsy authentication, thank you very much!

However, as far as Jennifer Aldridge is concerned, Home Farm still retains 'Manor' status, if the rose garden and the swimming pool are anything to go by. Though I'm not sure the barbecue patio is quite in keeping with her aspirations to 'old' money – I wish she'd just settle for a lichen-covered terrace with urns! Still, mine is not to question why – and I can quite see that a barbecue might induce Kate and her friends to have jolly teenage parties at home instead of disappearing for months on end with one knows not whom! But I'll never understand why she doesn't screen that ghastly silo with a decorative trellis of honeysuckle, though I fear the only thing to camouflage an eyesore like that would be a Russian vine scrambling all over it and they'd never get that past MAFF (Ministry of Agriculture, Food and Fish).

It is true I've had occasion to reprimand the Aldridges. Brian, for his arrogance over footpaths, country ponds and rutting deer; Jennifer, for having the temerity to call herself a writer and historian, when a more accurate description of her way of bending facts would perhaps be hack journalist!

But I forgive them much because they have had such problems with daughter Kate. Fortunately, my own relationship with Kate is more relaxed, not that I presume to be a surrogate parent or anything so intrusive – just a close friend and confidante who can be trusted at all times and in all situations to be objective, in a caring way. Which is why I felt rather let down when Kate

didn't contact me from wherever she was travelling to. I mean, it wouldn't have hurt her to phone. But that's teenagers for you!

Now that you've seen what constitutes Ambridge's neo-stately home, why not do a *volte face* and *renverser* towards Ambridge Hall, which Robert and I like to think represents something nearer to the real thing.

Isn't it fascinating how different people view things differently? Some have described the Hall as an 'eyesore' and a 'Victorian monstrosity' – well, all I can say is, 'They would, wouldn't they!' Fortunately, what they lack in taste and discretion has been more than made up for by my Ultimate Vision for the Hall.

When we bought it through the late Laura Archer's estate in 1986, the Hall looked . . . sad, but spiritually undiminished – broken, but unbowed. I relished the challenge of face-lifting this faded beauty, and with all my past experience in interior design it was merely a question of my eye and Robert's cheque book.

Today, you see mellow, yellow brick melding with autumn shades in shutters and paintwork overlooking elegantly re-landscaped gardens sweeping down to the River Am. Authentic architectural details include a hipped, tiled roof, a *demi-lune* fanlight and a tessellated tiled floor, and of course, the views are to die for!

Yes, I think the Hall is now a home the original owner (a local doctor) would have been proud of – if he'd had any taste, that is. And while we're on

Do drop in to Ambridge Hall – I offer a delightful guided tour of the house and garden including a short talk entitled 'Interior Design – the final solution'. (Leaflet at Reception.)

the subject, I wish to state that there is absolutely no truth in the ugly rumour that I had plans to install a swimming pool in the conservatory. No dedicated plantswoman would *dream* of committing such an act of vandalism, and anyway, I'm allergic to chlorine.

If you have time, and I have the afternoon off, I hope you'll stay for a glass of my Elderflower Petillant and a *langue de chat* on the terrace. But don't worry if you can't – there's lots more to see.

Which brings me to the subject of Grange Farm. Now, I have a confession to make – there are some properties in Ambridge that I would rather you avoided, and Grange Farm is one. It's enough for you to know that it is built on eighteenth-century foundations (of course!), which probably accounts for its crumbling brick and flaking rendering. Indeed, the general picture is best described as slurryesque. Of course, I'm not underrating the appalling treatment they've undergone at the hands of Simon Pemberton over the months, nor their courage and tenacity in recovering their position at Grange Farm against all the odds, but I'm afraid that despite his carousing with Brian Aldridge into the small hours, Joe Grundy just isn't 'Gentleman Farmer of the land-owning classes' material. But then, neither is Simon Pemberton, or he might have behaved with more humanity to the less fortunate!

I think this view of Grange Farm says it all.

St. Stephen's Church: note slight list to starboard.

Let us instead head for St Stephen's Church, pausing to espy charming Glebe Cottage, home of Shula and Daniel Hebden and going right back to Squire Lawson-Hope's day when it would probably have been regarded as a sort of playhouse for Lady Lettie (rather in the way Marie Antoinette played at shepherds and shepherdesses in her specially built village, though without such wanton decadence one hopes). How Shula manages to find time to keep the garden looking so delightful is a mystery to me, but I can only think she inherited her grandmother Doris's green fingers.

Looking at St Stephen's today, it's easy to see why the village is so fond of this living memorial to Ambridge history. Built on the remains of a seventh-century Augustinian church (oh dear!), it combines all the best elements of Norman, Early English and Perpendicular styles. But let us not fool ourselves – trying to keep various bits of St Stephen's in a perpendicular position has tested the ingenuity and purses of generations of church-goers.

I suppose the fault lies not in ourselves but in our foundations (yet again!), or at least in those of the bell tower, which has an interesting list to starboard of about six inches – due, no doubt, to those early cowboy builders hoodwinking the abbot into believing that they'd invented the prototype for the Leaning Tower of Pisa.

Well, it's been one thing after another – and here is just a selection:
1. Bells crashing though the floor.
2. Bats in the belfry – inevitable really, but sensibly allowed to remain there in order to eat the …

3. Death watch beetle! (Nothing like leaving Nature to do the dirty work for you!) I only wish Janet Fisher, our Vicar, would be as relaxed about the current bat invasion, but she seems enmeshed in her irrational phobia.

4. Bees. Yes, bees! Also in the belfry – lured out by Mike Tucker, apparently, and probably connected with one of his overwrought schemes for making his fortune.

5. Mice eating the hassocks, hymn books, organ stops, etc.

6. Dry rot, wet rot – I could go on and on.

Fund-raising is enthusiastically undertaken through various events and entertainments, many of my own devising, it has to be said – well, the more successful ones, anyway. But I'm afraid there *are* those who may not be motivated purely by the worthiness of the cause, as in the case of Jack Woolley and Cameron Fraser competing to pay for mending the church clock. I would never point a finger at Mr Woolley and I doubt if he's even heard of motive – he tends to operate more by instinct, which may account for some of his rather erratic decisions and, of course, his apparel.

No, I was actually referring to the Scottish gentleman who never set foot inside the church, or kirk (well, I never saw him there anyway), and misguidedly saw the whole project as a way of currying local favour when anyone could have told him that several evenings of 'Drinks on the house' at the Bull would have had the desired effect, and at a third of the cost.

I think my worst memory, church-wise, was at the rededication ceremony when, with everyone singing 'Jerusalem' (heaven knows why), the clock weights crashed to the floor, nearly killing William Grundy and necessitating the gathering's withdrawal to the village hall where William was comforted with hot tea and the contents of the WI's emergency biscuit tin. At least 'Jerusalem' had found a more appropriate venue!

If it hadn't been for Mr Pullen inciting the Over 60s to mutiny over the lack of toilet facilities in the church (their war chant of 'No more holding on!' still rings insidiously in the ears) I don't suppose anyone would have discovered that the foundations dated back to AD526. And as though that wasn't bad enough, Joe Grundy, morbid as ever, insisted on tolling the church bell to summon the villagers to witness Jason (builder, jack-of-all-trades and archaeological digger for the nonce) revealing a collection of bones and shards of pottery in the churchyard.

It was all getting very silly with hoards of architectural students and reporters cluttering up the place and, when an urn and some jewellery were found, I decided the time had come to step in, take matters in hand and go public on local TV.

For some reason, my interview was cut from the programme. I don't know why. No-one from the studios bothered to contact me to explain. Robert offered to ring them, but I said, 'No. I have the satisfaction of knowing I did a good job. One must remember that media people are deeply insecure – it's practically in their job description. No, I expect that interviewer can't forgive me for showing him up as rank amateur. Let's just leave it at that, Robert.'

Chrysanthemums suitable for flower carpet? I think not.

Robert looked away, and I could tell he was suffering for me from the way his face screwed up, as though in pain.

But you mustn't think it's all gloom and doom at St Stephen's – far from it. In fact the village holds some wonderful events there, like the Flower Festival, the highlight of which was my computer-designed flower carpet, designed to represent various Saints and animals.

I could never understand why Caroline was so unhelpful about my using Grey Gables software to create it – after all, I did wait until there was a lull at Reception.

Anyway, even Jill Archer admitted it was a triumph – that is, apart from one unpleasant element: resorting to petty larceny in the middle of the night when we ran out of red for St Martin's cow. I can't believe Kathy would have missed those petunias from the Bull – they weren't up to much anyway – but I still wake up in a sweat sometimes wondering if Higgs noticed the gap in his red carnations.

He's never said anything, but then he never does.

Of course, my most recent contribution to the interior embellishment of St Stephen's is via my square for the Easter Peace Quilt although, as it turned out, I was forced to go it alone, so to speak. The moment I heard that Hayley's playgroup was to have a hand in this project I realised that my creativity as a designer and my skills with an embroidery needle would be essential, if only to provide an oasis of vibrant colour amid the surrounding gloom!

I still think that either of my original ideas – a dove pattern, later super-seded by a silk rainbow with raised sheep to represent the Lamb of God – would have worked extremely well in a symbolic context. However, I sensed that Marjorie, Shula and Christine felt their squares were seriously threatened by my superior talents, so I offered a simple but significant Yin-Yang design, embroidered on sturdy hessian, as an alternative.

Unfortunately, hessian and old pillowcases don't hang very well together, texturally, so I withdrew my square – it clearly outclassed all the others anyway, even the playgroup's – and managed to persuade George Barford to frame it and hang it in solitary splendour in the nave. I had hoped it might even earn a place in the region of Grace Archer's memorial stained-glass window. I don't think that's asking too much – my embroidery would simply be enhancing a legend!

But I'm afraid the archdeacon, though most impressed by it, said that until permission was sought through the usual channels my square should remain out of sight in the vestry. Janet was very supportive, but it was rather disappointing at the time because Robert and I thought we might be translo-cating to Grimsby and I had intended to leave my Yin-Yang sign as a happy reminder to the congregation, every Sunday, of the harmony and enlighten-ment I like to think we brought to Ambridge. But I think Robert rationalised the situation with his usual tolerance: 'Look at it this way, Lyndy, one legend is probably enough for St Stephen's – two might be a surfeit of riches!'

Passing through the porch, and maybe checking out the new loo (all those halves of Shires must be taking their revenge by now), you enter the churchyard where on a good day – assuming Bert Fry has done a general tidy up – you will see gravestones dating back over the centuries and under which lie the ancient bones of those Great Families of Ambridge.

The Great Families of Ambridge

Someone once said that there have only ever been four great families in Ambridge: the Blowers, the Archers, the Forrests and the Gabriels. I don't know *who* said it, but it certainly wasn't a Grundy, as I'm sure you'll agree.

But, it *could* have been a Gabriel (they are wont to have a well-developed sense of self-worth) so, on a hunch, I hitched a lift to Borchester and tried to draw Nelson Gabriel on the subject of his ancestors over a portion of Quiche à la Shane and a full-bodied house red – available by the glass, I'm glad to say (one always needs one's wits about one where Nelson is concerned).

'Oh, what now, Lynda? Not more questions about my lineage, surely!'

'Well, you do belong to the House of Gabriel, you know, Nelson – something to be proud of, I'd have thought. Aren't you going to join me in a glass of this delicious house red? Remember – *in vino veritas*!'

'Not necessarily, Lynda. However, if you insist. How far back do you want to go?'

'Nelson, I've always believed in being as "far back" as possible, so fire away.'

'Well, there used to be many crafts and trades in Ambridge in the old days, and the early Gabriels were blacksmiths. A good blacksmith was essential. In fact, King Alfred is said to have honoured the smith above the tailor, when the latter went on strike.'

Nelson Gabriel: one of the ancient sons of Ambridge.

Could it be possible that the Gabriels go back as far as King Alfred, I queried.

'No, Lynda. Though I suppose it's possible that he might have burnt the cakes in the very forge fire of the very smith he had favoured, who might just have been a Gabriel. I believe the king had a low boredom threshold and a healthy appetite. He probably got fed up waiting for his war horse to be shod, fancied a snack and – Heigh-ho! Such are the trivia on which history relies!'

Though impressed by Nelson's way with an epigram, I refrained from comment, in case he got ideas above his station, but begged him to continue.

I was surprised to learn that Nelson comes from a long line of blacksmiths.

'Oh, must I? Oh, very well. The first Nelson Gabriel had a smithy where the garage used to be, and his motto above the door read: BY HAMMER AND HAND ALL ARTS DO STAND.'

Noble sentiments indeed! But I'm afraid I find it hard to believe that Nelson, of all people, is descended from great, muscle-bound men of toil, so I enquired as to what had gone wrong.

Gabriel Gabriel in a particularly uplifting moment...

'Lynda, please! Suave, elegant sophisticate I may be, but that doesn't mean I don't have iron in my soul, muscles in my genes and fire in my –'

He was obviously in some sort of perverse mind-set which only serious flattery could unravel, so I told him that brute force isn't everything, and that his real strength lies in his brilliance as a wit and raconteur. It worked like a charm!

'You think so? Good. Well, you may be surprised to know that we Gabriels had a white sheep in the family – one Gabriel Gabriel. He went about with long golden hair and long white robes, looking just like Jesus, though some say he didn't behave like Jesus. But, to the rest of the family he was just boring and, naturally, they felt he was undermining their reputation for wit, charm and humour and – other things.

'Moreover, wandering around the village looking like Jesus Christ was frowned upon by the Puritan authorities of the day, and could lead to charges of papistry and worse. In the end, they cut off his hair, dressed him in black and packed him off to the Americas with the Pilgrim Fathers, never to be seen again, thank heavens!'

I was riveted. What an *incredible* story!

'Ye-e-e-s, that's rather what I thought, Lynda,' he replied, and gave me one of his long, unnerving looks. But I didn't flinch, I merely persevered with a further question on the subject of blacksmiths and the Blower family.

'No, Lynda, I know what you're up to and you must *stop* trying to make preposterous connections between blacksmiths' bellows and blowing air into them. The early Blower was a local poet, but his descendant, Joe Blower, was a ne'er-do-well tenant farmer who was always at loggerheads with my father. Now, if you'll excuse me, I have a wine bar to run!'

...before 'going straight' with the Puritans.

Surely he wouldn't desert me now, just when I was about to peak!

'Don't be so melodramatic, Lynda! You're not starring in the village panto now, you know.'

I managed to overlook this irrelevance and calmed him down by deftly changing the subject to Walter Bloom, 1705 – a horticulturist, perchance?

'What? Good heavens, no! He was dyer – it says so on his gravestone, as you very well know. And the carpenter was called Mumford, hence the saying, 'A job for Mumford's', meaning a death is expected – and that could be any minute now, actually, Lynda, if you insist on continuing this ridiculous interrogation!'

And he stormed off to serve Elizabeth Pargetter a dry white wine and a prawn salad sandwich, muttering something like 'Wretched woman!' I must say I agree with him – Elizabeth can be very irritating, especially when competing with Julia Pargetter for the role of Lady of the Manor. I think she's probably at her best when she and Nigel are playing with Ellie May, but then, animals often improve the most unlikely people.

But who would have thought Nelson capable of such *puissance*? Momentarily getting in touch with his brawny heritage, I suppose, and nothing wrong with that, so long as he controls any unseemly outbursts – not everyone is as understanding as I.

Besides, he really mustn't feel any need to over-compensate, just because Julia Pargetter discovered red high heels in his wardrobe. Anyone *au fait* knows he wore them as second Ugly Sister, Gabriella, in *Cinderella*, and none of his fellow artistes is likely to forget the colourful language that accompanied his final exit, as he staggered off-stage muttering, 'Never again! As God is my witness!' – or words to that effect. And what was Julia Pargetter doing in Nelson Gabriel's wardrobe in the first place? This was pantomime, not a Whitehall farce. No! – don't say it! 'No thanks to Larry Lovell that it didn't decline into Greek tragedy!' – I couldn't agree more. But that still doesn't answer my question. Maybe one will pursue this further, later on.

Relieved to have deciphered the innermost secrets of two of Ambridge's Great Houses, I was still challenged by the other two, the Archers and the Forrests, linked by well-known blood-ties within recent history. Tom Forrest was the obvious key since his sister Doris had married Dan Archer, a young tenant farmer, and set up at Brookfield all those years ago.

'Us Forrests have got gamekeeping in our blood, you might say. My old dad, William, was gamekeeper to Squire Lawson-Hope, y'know, and we go back a long way – longer'n my arm anyway.'

We were in the kitchen at Keeper's Cottage, attractive in its own way, and aglow with brass knick-knacks on every available surface.

I had expected to see the odd brace of pheasant hanging picturesquely

Pru's jams, proving to be quite diverting.

from a smoke-blackened beam, but there was only the Lazy Susan. (Well, that's Joe Grundy's name for it, when he fondly recalls his late wife's occasional fall from grace. But as readers of the small ads. in *Country Living* will know, I'm actually referring to a suspended airing rack and this one was sporting several pairs of Tom's long johns.)

While he made some tea and buttered two slices of *white, sliced* bread (another illusion shattered!), I admired a small display of shotguns (all identifiable weapons, I'm sure) and an impressive collection of cups and trophies, demonstrating Tom's flair in the flower and vegetable garden, and Pru's power with pectin.

Indeed, I espied through the open pantry door, sagging shelves laden with jams, pickles and preserves, dating back many moons if the cobwebs were anything to go by and probably of vintage quality by now. Perhaps this would be my chance to do a test-and-tell comparison with Marjorie Antrobus's famous black-currant and rhubarb melange!

I discreetly enquired after Pru.

'Oh, my Pru's fine thanks, Lynda, all things being equal. That's her jam in there, y'know.'

Considering I'd been gazing longingly at it for the last ten minutes, I happily enthused about how delicious it must be, especially the blackcurrant and rhubarb!

'You're right, it is, *and* she's got them cups to prove it! And I'll tell you summat else – it's better than Freda Fry's and Marjorie Antrobus's put together!'

I realised I was entering a political danger zone here – the gloves were off, as Tom challenged my loyalty and the air seemed redolent with old rivalries, the pride and the passion. Which was all quite unnecessary, since all I wanted was a taste, or preferably a jar of Pru's jam! However, I decided to take up the gauntlet.

'Really! I was offered some of Marjorie's only the other day and excellent it was too.'

'Ah, well, there's excellent – and there's superb, in't there?'

'Yes, and comparisons are odious, but the proof's in the pudding, isn't it?'

'Yep, and out of sight is out of mind,' said Tom, slamming the pantry door shut.

I wondered for a surreal moment if Tom might be in the middle of reading a John le Carré spy novel and was acting out a coded conversation with me, to gain hands-on experience of the world of espionage.

But I decided that, interesting though this theory might be, it was more likely that he had simply decided that Pru Forrest's jam collection should remain intact for posterity, though viewings could be arranged by special appointment, and only after a rigorous selection process.

Relieved that I had not been out-manoeuvred, I realigned his thoughts and outlined for him my own theories about the origin of his family – how the name Forrest presumably comes from forebears who worked for an early version of the Forestry Commission, planting and tending the huge tracts of forest which covered the countryside. Later on, when various Land Acts ordered the clearance of woodland for pasture, their descendants were made redundant and forced to take up poaching to survive. Fortunately, an enlightened Squire Lawson-Hope took pity on these poor wretches and legitimised them by appointing them gamekeepers, and a family tradition was born.

I felt sure he would be awed by my presentation, but I hadn't bargained for the mesmeric effect it seemed to have on him. He remained silent for some moments and then seemed to nod his agreement, and I breathed a sigh of relief and, yes, triumph! However, when the silence that followed was suddenly punctuated by a loud snore, I doubted that Tom had been *quite* aware of everything I had said. But as he regained consciousness, it was obvious that he had grasped the salient points.

'What are you on about, Lynda? I don't know *why* we're called Forrest – we just are. And you wanna be careful what you says about folks' ancestors being illegitimate poachers. All I knows is that gamekeepin' goes back a long way, and it gets you close to Nature, and makes you a dab hand at a lot of things – like protecting animals and plants and understanding what makes 'em tick.

'And as for that insinuation about my parents, I knew *both* of 'em, and my ol' dad had proper morals and respect, and that's how Doris and me was brought up. And I'll tell you summat else, I ain't got no respect for poachers, especially after that business over Bob Larkin all them years ago!'

Horrified, I suddenly remembered having heard about Tom accidentally shooting Bob Larkin, poacher and rival, and the unpleasant legal ramifications that ensued.

How could I have been so tactless? And so out of character? It simply isn't in my nature to be insensitive, especially to a fellow follower of Nature's lore! Suitably humbled, I reassured him that I didn't care a fig about his shady past, that I've always thought of him as a fine, upstanding man of the woods, able to overcome all trials and tribulations, and incapable of an unworthy act. In any case, I really felt the Forrest family tree had been done to death, so what could he tell me about the Archers?

Tom's father – William Forrest, gamekeeper to the Lawson-Hopes. A man who clearly knew where he was going.

He seemed somewhat relieved to be granted a change of subject, and settled back in his chair to continue thus: 'Ah well, they've been around even longer – generations they been farming around Ambridge. Our two families have always been very close, helping each other out at every opportunity. Dan had a brother, Frank, went off to New Zealand and died there. His widow Laura – well, it was her estate you bought Ambridge Hall off of –'

I had to interrupt before he became bogged down in trivia and lost

Harvest at Brookfield Farm in the 1940s. Tom occasionally lent a hand in exchange for a pint of Shires at the Bull. (Another example of rural barter.)

sight of my main enquiry – did he know why they are called Archer?

He gave me what could only be described as a muffled glare, which I returned forthwith. He was now on his fourth slice of bread and butter, and still no sign of Pru's jam being disinterred. I couldn't have eaten a thing, of course, not with all that tension in the air.

Finally, I could bear the impasse no longer, and proceeded to explain my own theory, gleaned from Borchester Library's precious and much-thumbed copy of *Les Anciens Aphorismes Apocryphes d'Agincourt* by Bernard le Buveur de Burgundie, a passing chronicler of the time.

The Archers do indeed go back a long way – as far as the Hundred Years' War, to be precise. In fact, they were thought to be the very same Archers who, at the Battle of Agincourt, fired their arrows into the air to fall like rain onto the approaching French army, causing massive losses (those of you who saw Sir Laurence Olivier's wonderful Bardic film version of *Henry V* will remember that thrilling moment, underscored by Sir William Walton's portentous music). Sadly, it wasn't a moment I felt like sharing with Tom – he was having enough trouble staying awake, it seemed.

Well, of course, Henry V was delighted with the Archers' contribution to the eventual victorious outcome and asked some of them to stay on in France

Spot the Archer.

after the war, as part of a rehabilitation plan – probably an early blueprint for the *Entente Cordiale*. This they did, and were soon establishing themselves in the environs of Honfleur and Crecy, where they were known as Les Flècheurs, in recognition of their skill with a bow – *flèche* being the French for arrow. Later on, some returned to Ambridge, but the French name stuck and, in local dialect, became corrupted to Fletcher.

'So you see, Tom, the Archers are really the *Fletchers* – isn't that astounding?'

I was delighted to see that my theory appealed to him, because he awoke with a start and burst into gales of laughter, with not a glare in sight – an unexpected and most welcome mood swing.

'Oh Lor', now I've heard everything! I tell you what, Lynda, why don't you go and try that one out on Phil Archer – see what he has to say about it. Meantime, I reckon you deserve a jar of Pru's special blackcurrant and rhubarb jam after what you just been through.'

Early Archers/Fletchers struggling with fancy French farming implements.

And without further ado, he opened the pantry door, parted the cobwebs, and presented me with a large Kilner jar bearing the label 'September 31st, 1963'. Without question, this was a veritable antique – in jam terms, that is.

'There you are, Lynda. I reckon Pru would want you to have that, seeing as how you've just given me the best laugh I've had since I beat Bert Fry's marrows at the Flower and Produce Show.'

At last. The jar of blackcurrant and rhubarb jam I had long longed for, was in my grasp! This was a seminal moment.

I thanked him, declined his offer of an old pair of long johns to wrap it in, and placed it carefully in my saddlebag before he changed his mind.

And as I pedalled off towards Brookfield, I took comfort in the knowledge that I appeared to have redeemed myself quite successfully from my earlier *faux pas* because I could hear Tom belting out 'The Village Pump' in the distance. By the time he'd got to verse four, I knew I had made an old man very happy!

I found Phil Archer in the kitchen, surrounded by scraps of grey, leftover pastry, which no double Pip had had a hand in.

'Oh hullo, Lynda – what brings you here?' Good heavens! A first! I take it all back. (Please cross refer yourselves to 'A Village Walkabout'.)

I told him. He smiled thoughtfully and said, 'Well, that's a very interesting theory, Lynda, and I almost wish it were true. Because, you see, if the Archers really were the Fletchers, we might have avoided the Great Grundy Grudge!'

I was speechless, almost, apart from managing a croak of amazement.

'Oh yes, it's been much better since Simon Pemberton went, but you really can't talk about families like the Archers – sorry, Fletchers – without mentioning the Grundys. After all, the Grundys have been at Grange Farm for genera-tions, and Susan Grundy, Joe's wife, is buried in St Stephen's churchyard, as he will tell you proudly at the drop of a hat. But most importantly, the two families are linked by the terrible curse that the Archers are supposed to have put on the Grundys years ago.'

I was furious! This was very inconvenient. I had already written my chapter on the supernat-ural. I really didn't want to upset the structure of perfectly balanced prose by inserting spurious offerings from illegible Grundy archives, detailing which witch was sticking pins in poppets, and why, even if such documents existed.

Phil Archer still struggling today with agrotech devices!

Phil must have spotted my look of chagrin because, with unusual perception for a farmer, he said, 'I'm sure you could do with a cup of tea, Lynda – sadly, I can't offer you one – I've got to clear up this mess before Jill gets back, and then I'm off to a WI lecture on the "Gluten-free loaf – better results the home-made way".'

(I do wish Phil Archer would make up his mind whether to be a farmer or Delia Smith; this shilly-shallying with the question is absurd and I consider it morbid, unless, of course, one is a Grundy, when I suppose it would be almost *de rigueur*!)

Ever the canny farmer, Phil Archer must have read my expression and seen a way of passing the buck neatly back to his old enemy.

The Grundy family, thinking positive for once.

'Look, why not go and talk to Joe about it. There's nothing he likes better than a good old moan about the dreaded Archer clan – and you'll be making an old man very happy.'

Well, really! I'd already done that once today and it's not the sort of thing I intend to make a habit of, not even in the cause of literature. So what exactly was he implying? Probably better not to dwell on it.

However, this *is* Ambridge heritage we're talking about, and there's no getting away from the fact that Susan Grundy is buried in St Stephen's church-yard, or that, as the visitor will have already discovered, the surviving Grundys have left their indelible mark on the texture of village life (in much the same way as vandals paint-spraying graffiti on the village bus shelter, some might say – not that I'm one of them, you understand).

Yes, the Grundys *are* an inescapable fact of life in Ambridge and must be given their due, but that didn't prevent a sinking feeling at the prospect of interviewing Joe Grundy on 'How an ancient blood feud destroyed my life'.

In fact, I'd been putting the meeting off as long as possible in the cynical hope that an attack of Farmers' Lung might confine him to bed, and I certainly have no intention of being trapped in a bedroom with Joe Grundy – and with good reason!

I still have a vivid mental picture of the time when, while organising the entire village fete virtually single-handed, I was cut off at the zenith of my powers by a spot of back trouble. Fortunately, on the day of the fete, I was able to supervise the festivities from a litter, but it was during the hectic preparatory period, while I was busy issuing vital contingency instructions from my bed of pain to my rather limited rota of visitors, that Joe Grundy walked in, fresh from muck spreading.

Appalled, I stopped him in his tracks with a well-projected cry of, 'Joe, don't come one step nearer in those wellingtons! Either take them off, or stay by the door; I don't want mud all over the Wilton.'

Well, that was my first mistake. He grudgingly removed the wellingtons and approached my bed in his socks! I don't remember much after that. Everything went hazy as the fumes from his feet filled the room with a murky miasma. I do have a vague memory of a bunch of flowers clutched in a grimy hand – I'm not saying he's totally bereft of social skills (though one wonders from whose garden they came), but their scent was completely nullified by the noxious gases emitting from those socks.

Joe Grundy displaying his social skills with a knowing smile.

From that day on, I vowed I would never again set foot in a bedroom containing Joe Grundy. I do not intend to break that vow.

And anyway, how do I know I can give credence to anything he might have to say about our historical heritage after his disgraceful behaviour over 'Dan Archer's Diary'. This was a rather original idea of mine for giving our French friends in Meyruelle, our twin village in the Dordogne, a translation of a piece of local heritage namely, 'Dan Archer's Diary' which, it was believed, had survived to this day. This generous act was suggested with a view to enriching our *entente*. After much research into the subject I felt I was getting nowhere, when Joe Grundy appeared on my doorstep, clutching what he claimed was the 'authentic vital document'.

I should have smelt a rat when I read the entry dated 29 February, 1963: 'Saw Joe Grundy today, tolling up the road in rags and no shoes, since he had to sell his last remaining ferret. How gilty I feel, seeing this poor retch reduced to such bitter cercumstances! And all becos of my ancestors wicked and cruwel treetment of his four bears in days of olde!'

I recognised the style instantly as a melange of 'Christmas Day in the Workhouse' and 'The Hob Hound' ode and told him so. He retreated disconsolate, muttering, 'The Grundys will be revenged!' or some such drivel, and I considered the matter closed.

Which is why I felt I'd been completely manipulated into my current position, sitting in the Bull opposite Joe Grundy, separated only by a sticky set of dominoes.

'Your move, Missus,' he gasped, shaken by a sudden spasm of Farmers' Lung.

I insisted he made some effort to resist this compulsion to gamble, for just a few minutes, and let me help him to reveal the truth about the wronged Grundy clan. I suggested he should first use a handkerchief, sample a reviving drink, and then tell me all about it.

But he pushed away my mini thermos of hot lemon posset with honey undertones in preference for his original pint of Shires. One swig and, as though granted the gift of tongues, Joe burst into a moving account of his family from the Middle Ages until the present day.

Apparently, the earliest-known Grundys were recorded in Grundisberg, in Suffolk – yes, it actually exists, if my *Green Guide to Places Nobody's Ever Heard Of* is anything to go by. I did suggest to Robert that we might do a two-for-the-price-of-one weekend break to East Anglia, as seen in the *Sunday Times*, purely for research purposes, of course. But, without even looking away from his VDU, he said, "It's a dump, Lyndy, and very flat. Noel Coward said so.'

I didn't bother to correct him – most people know that Coward was referring to Norfolk – but I'm afraid Robert does have these occasional bouts of cognitive ignorance, so I hope the delightful inhabitants of East Anglia will look compassionately upon him.

The name Grundy is derived from a Danish word meaning ground – i.e. land. Thus, Grundisberg was 'the town built on the land of them who got there first, Missus, which just goes to show what a respectable lot they were, always having their *own* land from time irrevocable!' (Joe's words, *not* mine.)

And so the Viking Grundys landed in Suffolk (before anyone else), and founded their first settlement of Grundisberg. Of course they pillaged and plundered for a while to make their point to the local inhabitants who were actually quite relieved to be marauded by this vigorous flaxen-haired tribe. We have to remember that this was just at the end of the Dark Ages and most

Viking Grundys landing in Suffolk must have seemed like aliens landing to the unsuspecting locals.

The Grundys recorded their progress, rather crudely, on this ancient map which has somehow survived to this day.

of the population, especially of East Anglia, had become very depressed after so many years of misery and low light levels. In fact, behavioural research suggests that they were probably displaying the earliest-known signs of SAD (Seasonal Affective Disorder), and is it surprising?

The Grundys certainly livened things up for a bit, until they got bored with the locals being so compliant and decided to spread their disruptive influence farther afield. They headed inland through Cambs., Herts., Beds. and Bucks. towards Wilts. and Worcs., leaving a trail of havoc and many baby Grundys in their wake.

At last, worn out by their excesses, they settled in Borsetshire, around Felpersham (a loose corruption of Walpurgisnacht), where they introduced some rather interesting and noisy ritual-istic devil worship. I was astonished to hear this from Joe because, try as I might, the only interesting thing I could find in

Felpersham is the cathedral, though I agree about the noise, especially on market day.

It was here that they finally met resistance from one of the Archers (Fletchers, for the purist), newly returned, a hero, from the Hundred Years' War to find a large, grumpy Grundy on his farmstead.

Broadswords were drawn (arrows were considered bad form in the circumstances), and a lengthy duel continued 'for seven days and seven nights – a sennight it were called in them days, Missus.'

Of course, the lord of the manor, who couldn't stand any of them, turned a blind eye to all this – 'Oh Lord! Screaming serfs at it again! – best left to get on with it. Turn up the troubadour, O fair one!'

And before you could say 'Krumhorns and liripipes!' the Archers had regained their territorial strip, built a neat picket fence with a leylandii hedge for extra security, and the Grundys were sent packing to nearby 'Amridge – the oak ridge by the Am – standing in the shadow of Mount Ararat, Missus.'

The early Archer occasionally doubled as spear carrier.

I reminded him that we'd already established that Mount Ararat is in the Middle East – he really must stop confusing it with Lakey Hill.

But he wasn't listening. He rushed on with the next tranche of Grundy history which was the founding of the Hidden Village as a refuge from the Archers who had sent a posse of outriders to set up base on a tenanted farm in Ambridge, from which they were to mount the occasional midnight raid as a gesture of one-upmanship.

The lord of the manor was thoroughly bored by petty in-fighting among the lower orders.

The remains of the Hidden Village are *still* hidden actually – under a welter of decaying farm equipment and other Grundy paraphernalia carefully acquired over the years and now clothed in green sward I'm glad to say. But in the low sunlight of a winter afternoon, shadows are thrown across the grass, revealing the ghostly lines of ancient farm buildings where once those other Grundys lived and loved and loitered, with intent.

Lost in a reverie on the past, but reminded of the insistent present, I was struck with a brilliant idea: 'Joe, I'm going to organise balloon trips over the Hidden Village for visitors to Grey Gables. Think how thrilled they'll be to get a sighting of the lost Grundy heritage, while quaffing mugs of Kingston Black cider! We'll discuss finances later with Mr Woolley, but you could make a fortune! Oh, Joe, I'm so excited for you!'

To my utter amazement, he merely sniffed and said, 'Who needs any more outsiders gloating over the dispossessed victims of Archer greed? Eh? Answer me that!'

I decided not to, not yet anyway. For the moment, I was more interested in Joe's curious display of quiet good taste, especially as he has never been one to turn down the chance to make money and often in some of the grossest ways imaginable. He soon reverted to type, however, by informing me that he'd had fifty copies of the Ordnance Survey map run off and had drawn in a few lines in green, eco-friendly biro so that visitors could see where the Hidden Village is – hidden. All for £5 a time and cheap at the price, and I could sell them on Reception at Grey Gables for a small commission.

I'm afraid I had to scotch that idea immediately – I am, after all, a middle-management executive, not a salesperson of over-priced goods. But I do see myself as an enabler, so I suggested that Joe, himself, should run guided tours of the Hidden Village on fine winter days, say 9.00 a.m. and 3.30 p.m., Saturdays only, October to January, excluding Christmas and New Year. By appointment.

I won't repeat his unhelpful response to this, because, mercifully, it was completely muffled by Farmers' Lung.

It was time to get tough. Joe clearly had no intention of exploiting his assets in anything like a manner to satisfy the local Trading Standards officer, so I felt a little psychotherapy was called for.

'Joe, I'm hearing what you're saying, and what you're experiencing is the distress your ancestors must have felt, but it's a long time ago. Don't you think you're overreacting? Why not try relinquishing this feeling of resentment. After all, it's not really yours, is it? It's theirs. Let them own it.'

'What's theirs is mine, and what's mine's me own, and don't you forget it, Missus!'

A rather standard reaction from so dysfunctional a personality, I'm afraid. Sometimes it's very difficult to get through those defence mechanisms.

However, as though re-energised by this discovery (and another pint of Shires), he proceeded to tell me how the feud between the Archers and the Grundys eventually caused a terrible schism in the village, so much so that the two halves became known as Ambridge Superior and Ambridge Inferior.

'No need to ask which 'alf the Grundys were in, is there?' he wheezed. 'Mind you, *we* only had to pay one shilling and fourpence tax, while that other lot had to cough up five shillings – that were in old money, o' course.'

At last! A glimmer of positive thinking – could things be looking up for the Grundys? Well, no, actually, they couldn't! Because, naturally, Ambridge Inferior had the poorest land – heavy, unwieldy clay which to this day defies the plough.

Thus it was that, in desperation, the Ambridge Grundys secretly contacted their Walpurgisnacht (Felpersham) kith and got themselves invited to an evening of (Black)Arts and (Witch)Crafts, which included a demonstration of poppet-making for beginners. There was at the time a huge demand for these waxen images, since witchcraft was still big business, so the Grundys, ever quick to spot an opportunity, rushed back to Ambridge to set up a cottage industry, producing hundreds of wax poppets which they sold on to various local witches at a handsome profit.

Unfortunately, their supply of wax (job lots of monastery candles, sold off by Henry VIII during the Reformation) started to run out and ruin stared them in the face, yet again.

Just when the bailiff and his men were about to lay claim to the few remaining sticks of Grundy furniture (this was before the era of reclining armchairs), a Grundy child was spotted making mud pies in the filthy squalor of the farmyard, and it was realised that the cursed clay soil of Grange Farm was, after all, to save the day. Wax-modelling *Grundy clientele.*
skills were adapted to moulding figures from clay but, since clay was more suitable for making larger figures, the poppets grew into gnomes, and the first garden gnome industry was born.

There are probably priceless remains of pointy hats and fishing rods in gardens all over Borsetshire at this moment, just waiting to be unearthed by people in anoraks and shell suits.

By the time Oliver Cromwell came to power, Grange Farm Gnomes was a thriving business, and the day came when the Grundys made an appointment to see Squire Lawson-Hope to make him an offer he couldn't refuse – to purchase the Archer farm tenancy. At last they could own their land, this time in up-market Ambridge Superior, and put the Archers in their place once and for all.

As it happened, the Squire couldn't make up his mind whether he was a Roundhead or a Cavalier. He loved dressing up in curly wigs, frills and furbelows but didn't like the crippling Cromwellian taxes, so he settled for sombre black attire by day and kept the drag for after hours – at least, one assumes that was what he was doing.

Note the significant use of the Lawson-Hope motif in these pictures.

With Grundy gold he could have 'been himself' and saved on wardrobe space at the same time, and he would have done had it not been for – you've guessed it – the Archer Curse!

'Yep, it were an Archer what got there ahead of us and he upped and told the Squire that the Grange Farm gnomes were tainted with witchcraft, 'cos they were really poppets masquerading as garden gnomes, and the Grundys were nothing but a bunch of slummocky warlocks.'

The Squire, unconvinced, checked the story out with a Forrest (of course), who said, 'True enough, Squire, yer 'onour. Them Grundys be a welly-swatched lot o' yawnups. They'm allus been trouble – but what can you expect, with their breed and seed. Bad'uns and allus 'as been.'

I had the distinct impression that by deliberately using archaic Borsetshire dialect, Joe was hoping to throw my rather limited shorthand into disarray. And he might have succeeded, had it not been for my Diploma in Semi-Obsolete Dialects of Great Britain, which has been invaluable in my rural researches over the years. No translation can do justice to the richness of the above example of seventeenth-century peasant bigotry, so I will leave it unadulterated by a modern, if sensitive, pen.

Sadly, the Grundys were soon to feel very inferior indeed: the Squire, probably to curry a favour or two, reported them to Cromwell's men who made a dawn swoop and confiscated all their possessions, gnomes included. They were only just able to afford a passage to America, along with Gabriel Gabriel, who was glad to have someone to talk to, and was naturally familiar with obscure dialect anyway. They finally settled in Massachusetts and felt much more at home, selling garden gnomes to the witches of Salem – well, everything's bigger in America, isn't it?

At last I was able to congratulate Joe on the Grundys getting a result for the family.

'Ain't done me no good 'as it? Any more'n the other branch of the Grundys what got deported to Oz – Oztralia to you, Missus – in the convict ships.'

In my quest for detailed historical accuracy, I felt it my duty to ask if they might have been sheep-stealing criminal friends of Josiah Goodall by any chance.

By now, Joe was gazing mournfully and meaningfully into his empty glass, giving a very good impression of a broken man. Thank heavens I have witnessed this performance on a number of occasions, both on and off the stage of the village hall, so I remained unmoved. But a rapid refill of Shires lightened his demeanour considerably, and he proceeded to reel off a whole list of incidences of the Archer Curse on his family, dating back to the First World War, when Dan Archer 'cheated' his father out of Weston Farm. Since

Joe produced this picture of himself and his father at Weston Farm. (I simply don't believe it.)

I've never heard of Weston Farm, and I couldn't face unnecessary side-tracking, I decided to ignore its existence, except to agree that 'it were the start of the rot' for Joe personally.

When his beloved wife Susan died – at this point, he affected a maudlin tear or two, embellished with the oily rag he called a handkerchief – he was left to bring up Alf and Eddie: 'one a rogue, the other a villain – well, they'd inherited the curse an' all, see.'

And another thing, what about my Alf's Hedge, what were handed down to him from the Dark Ages? That David Archer tried grubbin' it up that time – you had one of your bloomin' campaigns against it.'

I considered for a long moment, consulted my *Dictionary of Old, Middle and Easily Corruptible English Words*, and decided that he probably referred to Aethelwold's Hedge – originally sited along the north-west side of Willow Farm. I suppose it would have been quite convenient to corrupt Aethelwold into Alf, after all, it is a bit of a mouthful, but even if the hedge was handed down to Alf Grundy, he couldn't have thought it was worth even the odd handful of bonemeal judging by its sorry state today. I didn't fancy explaining to Joe that he was confusing Aethelwold's Hedge with the less ancient one I saved from the jaws of David Archer's mechanical digger, aided and *abetted* by my loyal friends at the Borchester Environment Trust (BET to its chums). But I was touched that he remembered that triumphant day, and told him that the 'Restoration of Alf's Hedge' could well find its way onto my campaign list.

He ignored this gesture with another sally about when Phil Archer *deliberately* caught him burying a dead sheep in shallow ground, at the risk of polluting the water supply. 'Bloomin' cheek! Can't tell me nothing about water hereabouts, specially on Grange Farm. I had this vision, see, Missus!'

Apparently, Joe's father had appeared to him in a dream, telling him that there was spring water on the farm, if only he could find it. Try as he might, the two prongs of the twitching stick remained inert and he gave up, claiming, as usual, that the land was cursed. However, the result of another spot of illicit dead animal interment, this time in Clarrie's garden, revealed a miraculous spring gushing forth. His then landlord, the dreaded Cameron Fraser, sensing a viable market, actually authorised the Grundys to bottle the water, but he wasn't so keen to finance the bottling and labelling process so yet another Grundy project came to naught.

I asked him if he blamed Simon Pemberton's disgraceful treatment of the Grundys on the Archer Curse.

'Course I do! Just another example of injustice. And all because of them Archers taking what was rightfully ours in the first place. All down the years it's been goin' on – I ain't told you the censored bits – they'd make your 'air curl, alright!'

It was then that I saw my role of rescuer quite clearly – Joe could not be allowed to overlook the kindness shown to him by the Archers, and indeed the entire village, during those terrible months of persecution by the unspeakable Simon.

I reminded him how Shula had stood up for the Grundys at the tribunal and how indeed fervently he and the whole family had expressed their gratitude and appreciation. He seemed confused, a man struggling between truth and fiction. Only I could liberate him by revealing 'The Truth about the Archers'. But how would he take it? Should I risk his violent reaction? Or his tears of gratitude? Frankly, I didn't care, and anyway, I'd be doing him and everyone in Ambridge an enormous favour if it would stop his irrational behaviour.

I took several deep breaths to soothe my aura and announced that I had something to tell Joe which could change his life, if he was big enough to accept it in the right spirit.

I told him of my theory about the Archers really being the Fletchers and how standard practice regarding curses demanded authentic nomenclature from both parties for full implementation to be accomplished. No flicker of comprehension altered the grim set of his features, but I discovered that by economising on syllables I could produce a relatively simple formula:

'If the Archers' *real* name is Fletcher, it follows that the Archer Curse is considered to be null and void. Therefore, the Grundys no longer need to have a Grudge, because the Curse is not valid. QED.'

Joe looked appalled. 'What? You mean I spent all these years fretting under a curse which don't really exist, 'cos they got the name wrong?'

Had I gone too far? Was the realisation that he was a free man, and so was Eddie, and that the whole family could start to live a normal life, probably for the first time in living memory, too much for his fevered brain?

As if in silent response to my equally silent question, he rose unsteadily – he had consumed a great deal of Shires while in a very emotional state – and weaved his way to the door of the Bull, exiting loudly, but without a word of thanks. I wasn't surprised. This sort of thing is quite usual in rural circles, and I must warn the visitor to Ambridge not to expect very much from anyone in dirty wellingtons, green ones excepted of course.

That's another piece of Ambridge history and heritage neatly accounted for, providing an intimate insight for the visitor into those aspects of village life not normally discussed in the average guide book.

The Grundys and the Archers – three generations of two families at war.

Which is why I intend to ignore Clarrie Grundy's hysterical letter to me, demanding to know why I had upset Joe. He had refused to get out of bed and Doctor Locke had diagnosed chronic depression – without the Archer Curse to complain about, Joe had nothing left to live for, and it was all my fault for 'making an old man very unhappy!'

Typical! I sent some flowers and my copy of *101 Ways to Make a Fast Buck – The Green Way!*, by Seth Zimmerlinden, which I can highly recommend to visitors to Ambridge – it's crammed with good sense. I'm sure Joe will find something there to cheer his indomitable spirit and maybe show him the ecological way to self-improvement – but I shan't hold my breath!

Ghoulies and Ghosties

And things that go bump in the night

I love that quotation, don't you? It's so wonderfully evocative and somehow ... Scottish! And as the Bard knew only too well, the Scots were particularly sophisticated in the occult department, if their unkind treatment of Macbeth is anything to go by.

Anyway, I've always been fascinated by the supernatural, and I don't include science fiction or extra terrestrials which, in my opinion, are merely a pretentious excuse for the film industry to indulge its penchant for special effects.

No, what intrigues me is that humankind seems to have a manic predisposition to frighten the life out of itself. You have only to tell children the story of Hansel and Gretel – which, I'm glad to say, is not something I do with great frequency – to see from their faces that the witch definitely wins hands down in that one.

And so to the supernatural, for want of a better word, in the Ambridge context.

I suppose my first 'sighting' was a couple of years after Robert and I moved into the Hall. Shula was showing us round the newly completed barn conversions and I had been warned by Marjorie Antrobus, who had already sensed something cold and sickly in the atmosphere there. (I've often wondered about Marjorie's African background *à propos* witch doctors and the like, and I hope to interview her later on the subject.)

My fears were confirmed by Tom Forrest and Walter Gabriel who had seen a strange shadow on the premises. A hasty visit to Borchester Library revealed that as far back as the Civil War, a wounded soldier had holed up on that very spot and died. Obviously, his tragic spirit had been disturbed by the building work, and are we surprised, what with all the dirt and noise those contractors made, not to mention blocking off the road at the most inconvenient times?

Add to this the recording of strange phenomena on the site for many years plus the fact that, only a few days later, a mysterious light was seen in the 'empty' building before it was burnt to the ground and I think I can rest my case. Indeed, I think Ambridge is very lucky that this sad spirit didn't decide to burn down the entire development!

Of course, the cynics were ready with cries of 'faulty wiring', but how was it that a seventeenth-century coin was found in the burnt-out rubble next day? Was the young soldier hoping to slake his thirst with a last pint of shires at the Bull, and never quite made it?

What *is* clear is that Ambridge, deep in the crossfire of the Civil War and just up the road from the Battle of Hassett Bridge, must have been refuge to many brave men who died for their cause, whichever it may have been.

Which brings me to Ambridge's most celebrated ghost, the Little Drummer Boy, whose cause may have recently fallen into dubious Grundy hands. However, we know that on 14th June 1642 the Earl of Essex's men, exhausted after the Battle of Hassett Bridge, did stop off at the Bull and there found the dying boy with his arm sliced off. Some say that in his good hand he clutched a half of Shires and it was this that finally did for him, but he is much remembered – every time a half of Shires is consumed, in fact! The

The only illustrated recorded sighting of the Little Drummer Boy.

plaque to him in the Bull's Hassett Room restaurant, unveiled on its opening, commented on the cannonball he reputedly dislodged and sent crashing through the floor.

But who or what is it that makes the tapping noise in the Bull's wainscot during times of stress? Is it the Little Drummer Boy calling to be released back to his ghostly regiment? Is he in some strange time warp and will he have to go through the whole agonising process again?

I sincerely hope not because, frankly, I think Sid and Kathy have quite enough to cope with, and the thought of the Grundys trading off yet more fake Civil War memorabilia – like funny Cavalier feathered hats (just after turkey-plucking time, incidentally), and bits of armour made from melted down milk bottle tops – is too depressing to contemplate. Though of course, when you think of their forebears, it's hardly surprising!

But let us look at the whys and wherefores of it all.

Well, I suppose it's all rooted in ancient superstition, a word which has its own roots in the Latin *superstites*, meaning survivors – no, I couldn't see the connection to begin with, but a little applied semantics and common sense indicates that, of course, these old beliefs and magic rituals have survived from ages past, and we are left today with the fascinating remnants. Since moving to Ambridge, I frequently see *myself* as a survivor (though *not* a remnant) which is my way of facing all the trials and tribulations of village life, the constant frustrations, humiliations and disappointments (you name it) to be overcome, despite everything.

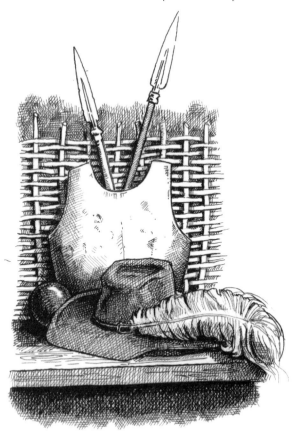

This memorabilia is far too upmarket for the Grundys. Did Richard Locke leave it lying around?

Somehow, it felt right to explore this whole exciting perspective further. Could I have some personal metaphysical bonding with a past aura? Was my subconscious instinct pointing me somewhere, and if so, where?

I looked around Ambridge for a likely answer. Could Marjorie Antrobus, with her possible voodoo past, provide a link? Or Tom Forrest, with his woodsman's feel for the unexplained and his known psychic experience at the barn conversion? Even young Kate Aldridge, a former traveller herself for some months, might have some useful contacts among the New Age brigade – known disciples of Brother Cadfael and all things Druidically mystical, from Balm of Gilead to Glastonbury Thorn.

I sought Kate out in a customary haunt – hanging over the rotting five-bar gate leading to semi-derelict Arkwright Hall, trying to look inconspicuous while smoking something faintly illegal and untidy-looking. When I broached the subject of her past connections, she merely smiled, somewhat mystically I thought, and mumbled, 'You should talk to Mr Pullen.' Good heavens! Strange indeed that Kate should be in touch with him when one sometimes wonders if she's even in touch with herself. But, as a former young person myself, and one who carries the burden of being misunderstood *even to this day*, I felt it only fair to make the usual allowances.

For visitors to the village who are unfamiliar with such details, Mr Pullen is one of the Great Mysteries of Ambridge. He has never been known to speak; some say because he hasn't anything interesting to say and he is really one of the Great Bores of Ambridge; others, that he is a Silent Seer, whose notoriously weak bladder caused such agitation at the Over 60's Super Splash at Grey Gables.

I prefer to think of him as a sort of human chakra, or way in to the secret world I was trying to investigate. Sitting in his cosy living-room, I was fortunate indeed to discover his secret, and finally persuaded Mr Pullen to *speak!*

'Don't talk to me about the bloody supernatural! I've inherited all that rubbish from me Granny Gertie. She were a genuine Romany – gypsy to you – and she used to drag me round all the fairs in her vardoe – caravan to you – when I were a kid. I had to polish her bloody crystal ball – a penny a time mind, I weren't daft!' (Oh dear! Such materialism in one so young!) 'Well, if you asks me, all this superstition lark come down from ancient Egypt. Stands to reason, dunnit? You write the word Egypt – cover the letter E – that leaves you with gypt – short for gypsy innit?'

In an attempt to divert Mr Pullen from sharing his apocryphal theories on ancient hieroglyphics I enquired further about his extraordinary grand-mother and her ancient connections.

Granny Gertie in her younger days was very active on the travelling fair circuit.

'Well, she had all these daft old sayings, like, "See hay, money today. See straw, money to draw."'

I assumed this referred to the harvest season and paying off the workers, but Mr Pullen was obviously on a roll, oratorically speaking, and would brook no interruption.

'That's right. Stands to reason, dunnit? Nothing supernatural about that!'

I tried appealing to his sense of family by asking if he had any happy memories of his grandmother, but the mere idea sent him purple in the face.

'You must be joking! I hated the old besom! It's 'cos of her I got me affliction.'

Rumour has it that he is very bitter about his bladder problem, but I never dreamed that I should be granted the privilege of hearing why.

'I reckon 'twas all that bloody dandelion tea she forced down me. Either that, or she put a curse on me – I wouldn't put anything past her, the bloody ol'...'

Granny Gertie assembles her family for a pot of dandelion tea.

At this point, I felt it safer to conclude the interview, as Mr Pullen made a beeline towards the bathroom, no doubt overcome by unpleasant memories of his grandmother.

As I slipped out of the kitchen door, I wondered if my unlocking Mr Pullen's powers of speech would now enhance his social life. Or would life's irony destroy his status as a Silent Seer. Only time will tell.

But his miraculous outburst encouraged me to forage further, and I next found myself braving the environs of Grange Farm in the hope of picking Eddie Grundy's brains – and I use the word loosely! Within seconds, I realised that Eddie hadn't a clue about anything supernatural outside *The X Files*, and he soon disappeared to the cellar, 'to give the Hob Hound his dish of Kennomeat, Missis! Tee! Hee!'

At which point I started violently as the door burst open and in staggered Joe Grundy, looking like something out of a Victorian melodrama. It was an uncanny, almost spiritual moment, for both of us, I like to think, because I had been wondering what to offer for my next theatrical production and in his simple, rustic way, Joe Grundy had given me the answer. Yes, *Murder in the Red Barn*! – well, unless I have a better idea, of course.

Already feeling much encouraged by Joe's somewhat awesome mien, I ventured to question him about matters mystical in and around Ambridge.

Needless to say, his immediate response was, 'What's it worth then, Missus?' Yet another glaring example of the farmer's obsession with the material! Isn't it enough to have the privilege of tending the land and husbanding the crops and beasts, in touch with Nature and the seasons at the most intimate level? I think Virgil catches my drift to perfection in the *Georgics* (II 458) when he states: *O fortunatos nimium, sua si bona norint, I Agricolas!*

Well, I have to say that these days I rarely carry cash. I like to travel light when cycling, and instead of filling my basket with over-priced, dreary convenience food from the village shop, I prefer to gather Nature's gifts from field and hedgerow – nettle soup and mushroom rissoles cost practically nothing and, despite the hours of preparation involved and the unwelcome, but necessary, expense of a manicure at Underwoods afterwards, they are so much more … interesting!

Of course, Joe laughed uproariously when I proffered my credit card so, undeterred, I tried bartering – an age-old country practice – but he spurned my offer of bicycle clips and even my trusty length of baler twine, supposedly indispensable to all farmers, left him unmoved.

I'm told this is a genuine photograph of the White Lady of Loxley Barrett.

In desperation, I finally signed the back of an old Milk Marketing Board envelope as an IOU for a pint of Shires and a meat pie at the Bull. By now, I had serious doubts about the validity of anything thus extracted from the wretched man, but needs must when the Devil drives! (A *bon mot* if ever I heard one!)

During the next few hours, I was to discover that Joe Grundy's other great obsession is Death. He took great delight in telling me that if I ever happen to be in the same room as a corpse I should not look in the mirror, because I'll see the image of 'another dead 'un'; indeed, there used to be a path running from Grundy land to St Stephen's churchyard called Corpse Way, because coffins were carried along it for interment (one dreads to think how much the then Grundy charged per coffin!).

'And what about that there Ann Timmins, eh? Her what drowned herself in

the Am years ago, after searching in vain for her lost sweetheart, eh? I reckon 'tis her what haunts the Am, down by Long Meadow – you seen that blue light flickering? That's her!'

I foolishly reminded him that it could just as easily be the White Lady of Loxley Barratt – a particularly anaemic ghost – or even the Hob Hound. 'Oh no, you'd know him – there's always a high wind a-blowing as he runs with the wild Devil horseman towards his prey.' There then followed 25 emotional verses of 'The Hob Hound' ode, punctuated by howling impressions from Eddie on guitar in the cellar.

Exhausted, I managed to interrupt the 26th verse with an enquiry about place names connected with the mysterious. Seemingly unable to break his poetic mode, he ranted on, 'Ah well, there's Hob Acre at Sawyer's Farm and Hob Meadow at Valley Farm – that's more'n likely where he caught up with his victim! And then, o'course, there's the Cat and Fiddle.'

A strange light in the trees at Hob Meadow. Ann Timmins or an extra-terrestrial?

I reminded him that while I had agreed to buy him a drink at the Bull, I drew the line at the Cat and Fiddle as well, fond as I am of Sean.

'Please yerself. Though I ain't no snob; I don't mind where I drink. But that ain't what I mean. Oh no! I mean the *Cat and Fiddle!* Eh? Think about it, Missus!'

Much nodding and winking ensued, some of a rather lewd nature, and I decided it was time to leave. I thanked Joe who, having lost interest, was now transfixed by a mortuary scene in *Casualty*, and I waved a sympathetic hand to Clarrie as she appeared, laden with shopping, but still managing to look pert and plucky.

It seemed the optimum moment to raise the worrying

Joe Grundy as the Grim Reaper.

question of Joe's morbid fantasies. 'Oh, that! You don't wanna take no notice of him, Mrs Snell. Y'see, he once played the part of the Grim Reaper in a Mystery Play and if you ask me, he ain't never got over it. I think it's affected him very deeply, see. He can be quite sensitive, at times. No, I know what you're thinking, but it's true. He got all soppy and sentimental when I told him about *me and Tom*."

She didn't look too pleased at the alacrity with which I leapt onto my bike, called goodbye and pedalled off towards Nightingale Farm. Frankly, I didn't feel up to Clarrie regaling me with yet another graphic account of the time, or even *times*, she was kissed by Tom Cruise when she co-starred (!) in *Isabella – an Orphan Jilted*. I don't really mind – heaven knows, she needs some fantasy in her life! But I think a little more sensitivity wouldn't come amiss; after all, remarks like 'you *extras* just didn't know what you were missing!' are not easy to swallow, even to seasoned players like myself.

I arrived breathless and parched at Nightingale Farm, but hopeful that in the warm, civilised atmosphere of the drawing-room, I might gain some further insight into the tortuous challenge I was facing.

Now, there have been occasions when I have been disappointed in Marjorie Antrobus and I feel it only fair to enumerate them:

1. Her churlish refusal of my offer of Ambridge Hall's grounds for the village fete.
2. The time she managed to run her car into Ambridge's old and much cherished finger post. True, it was as result of that that I set up HOOF (Hands Off Our Finger Posts) and won the day, but it could have been very ugly.
3. Her extraordinary behaviour during my production of *Pot Pourri*, when she deserted her organ in a huff and left Nelson and me to sing our Coward duet *a cappella*.

But, despite the above, I have found her general attitude to village life to be quite acceptable and one can't fault her as a fellow dog lover or provider of home-made scones and jam which, considering the lack of hospitality at Grange Farm, I was really looking forward to. And I was not disappointed. Over a pot of Earl Grey and a dish of buttery crumpets, our discussion took some interesting turns. After hotly denying my suggestion that the African mask on the drawing room wall, above the crossed Masai spears, might have been a gift from her witch doctor, she assured me that she had always regarded the supernatural as rather suspect, not to mention un-Christian.

I knew I must tread carefully here, since Marjorie is a lay reader and member of the PCC, as well as being a highly respected pillar of St Stephen's and the WI. So, with the utmost tact, I asked if she knew of any exorcisms recorded in St Stephen's archives. I was naturally surprised by her heated reaction.

'Lynda, really! I think you should talk to Janet about such things, it's not for me, a mere lay person, to say. However, if you insist, I do remember Martha Woodford telling me that in Penny Hassett, in about 1734, there was an invisible witch, possibly Mother Horsfell, who was smoked out of the parsonage by burning a mixture of hemlock, sloe, rosemary and rue.

In fact, Martha did hint that her home, April Cottage, was haunted by Florrie Hoskins, another invisible witch. Don't you remember a

Florrie Hoskins feeding some of her unusual pets.

few years ago, how Eddie and Snatch Foster pretended to be Florrie's ghost at the window? Poor Martha was terrified, though she did turn the tables on Kate Aldridge and William Grundy when they tried a similar trick at Halloween – she simply said that she often communicated with ghosts and even shared the occasional meal with Florrie Hoskins! That soon got rid of them, although personally, I always thought there was more to that remark of hers than met the eye.'

I'm afraid I was almost quivering with excitement. Was Marjorie about to reveal some more of the confidences of her late friend and rival in affairs of the heart?

Topping up her tea, I persuaded her to elaborate further.

'According to Martha, Florrie Hoskins had some sort of invisible ladder to get into difficult places and was accompanied by a full range of fairies, cobs, knops and flibbertigibbets [I always thought that meant something *quite* different!] all screaming and pestering and generally behaving extremely badly towards anyone they took a dislike to. Another thing, she planted laurel by her front door, you know, and so did Walter Gabriel, he even had rowan leaves carved above the lintel – to keep away evil, apparently. I must say, I thought it was a silly superstition, but Martha was a real countrywoman, so I would never argue with her.'

Cops, knops and flibbertigibbets up to their tricks.

She was indeed, and if one adds to all this the fact that her charming cottage garden had a large bed of cow parsley, also known as Devil's parsley, I think we can say without doubt, that Martha Woodford must have absorbed some of the magical atmosphere of that cottage and was probably influenced and enlightened by it. Of course, I didn't dream of confiding this to Marjorie, but I was thrilled that she had opened up so unexpectedly, and as a little reward for her co-operation I told her of my amazing breakthrough with Mr Pullen.

'What do you mean, you've given back Mr Pullen the gift of speech? My dear Lynda, Mr Pullen has been talking for years – in fact his favourite phrase, as everyone in the Over 60s Club knows, is "Where's the lav?" I think it's probable that he simply hasn't chosen to speak to *you!* And no doubt he has his reasons. And now, if you'll excuse me, it's time for Portia's walk.'

With that, Marjorie neatly flicked any remaining scone crumbs onto a tea plate for Portia to lick clean, something I would *never* permit *my* Afghan, Hermes, to do. (I'm glad to say that Hermes, while being a late developer, is finally getting over his problems with the piano leg and the duvet, and even manages not to get excited by leftover nettle soup and bean curry.)

I left Nightingale Farm with my mind in turmoil. I had already forgiven Marjorie's bad temper – she was obviously regretting bending her Christian principles by discussing the occult – but I can't imagine *what* I've ever done to Mr Pullen to make him send me to Coventry for the last ten years; nothing Christian about *his* principles, it would seem! But then, I'm accustomed to villagers misunderstanding my good intentions, and I suspect Mr Pullen of listening to gossip on some of those long, pub-ridden coach trips to Lytham St Anne's with the Over 60s.

Nevertheless, I was strongly tempted towards the conclusion that Martha Woodford could even have been a white witch, perhaps forming a small coven with Walter Gabriel (they were known to have been quite friendly over the years). Did she, Medea-like, gather 'simples at midnight' with which to brew herbal remedies for such ailments as Farmers' Lung, only to see Joe Grundy as living proof that they didn't work?

Exhausted by these and other imponderables, I sought diversion in my own garden at the Hall where, as if to welcome my return, there had appeared a fairy ring of mushrooms in the lawn. Closer investigation disclosed a cluster of puffball mushrooms, or bunts (possibly the same word as bun, or bunt, for a rabbit's tail). They were also connected with pucks or goblins, and the smoking puffball, when ejecting its ripe spores, suggested the somewhat crude though ethnic name of puckfist – meaning goblin's fart!

More confusion! Were the good fairies inviting me to cull their delicious field fare, or were the less co-operative goblins merely mocking my endeavours?

Still reeling from these somewhat lavatorial images, I felt the need to spend some more time closeted in Borchester Library, where I am known, fortunately. Here I discovered that there were indeed several degrees of sorcery, used for either good or evil. Sociologically, it served to consolidate questions about the supernatural world and how human beings related to it, while psychologically, it could establish a sense of control over nature and the uncertainties of seasons, disease and natural phenomena.

So if a witch/wise woman/midwife/agony aunt was capable of producing herbal remedies for sundry ailments, and charms and advice for the love-lorn, why not blame her for the failure of harvest, or drought, let alone the Black Death, the Wars of the Roses and even the worst excesses of the French Revolution?

Although the Church condemned witchcraft – 'You shall not permit a witch to live' (Exodus 22:18) – people still consulted witches and superficially Christianised their activities by inscribing the Lord's Prayer on a piece of paper inserted inside their shoe as a protective amulet (and, of course, to save on shoe repairs!).

As if all this hypocrisy wasn't enough, it was also laced with sexism, since the male-led orthodox religion conveniently regarded women as being most susceptible to the Devil's blandishments. It was quite usual to apply various tests to suspect witches like pricking the body for insensitivity to pain (the Devil's mark) and the dreaded water test, or ducking stool, when if a

Witch-ducking in the Am, supervised by Squire Lawson-Hope on a Puritan day, judging by his apparel.

witch sank when thrown into the village pond, she was considered innocent, if she stayed afloat, she was guilty.

No wonder witches were inclined to lie low and let themselves go, appearance-wise. Hardly much incentive to keep one's hair and skin looking good when the rest of the village might be 'hell-bent' (sorry, another *bon mot* – couldn't resist it) on throwing one into the pond at any moment – especially when one considers what *else* got thrown into village ponds of the day!

This could also explain their fondness for animals – cats, of course, preferably black, but also the less popular species like toads, bats, newts, snakes and spiders – not merely to help in their valuable work, but from a genuine empathy with fellow minority groups. The Bard said it all in *Macbeth* (IV.i.14) – I *think* it's safe to mention the title in print:

> *Eye of newt and toe of frog,*
> *Wool of bat and tongue of dog.*

(No! Get *down*, Hermes! This was a *different* dog!)

Hermes was unhappy about this picture, but...

I'm afraid all this injustice was really getting to me. And then, just when I thought I couldn't bear another heartrending example of Mediaeval misogyny, I came across the amazing, though not totally authenticated, legend of Mother Keech, the Wise Woman of Waterley Cross who, in 1347, promised to hand over to the Devil the next new-born baby if he would save the village from the local baron's tyranny. But the Devil demanded a kiss to seal the bargain and, although peace was restored for a while, Mother Keech, very foolishly in my opinion, tried to cheat by hiding all the new-born babies in her spare cauldron. Well, everything went horribly wrong because the Devil was, naturally, not too thrilled with this and the mark of his kiss turned black and erupted into hundreds of black spiders that wiped out the entire village. However, as she lay dying, Mother Keech managed to grab a passing spider – I suppose she didn't care by now – stuff it into a hole in the roof beam and plug the hole with a handy peg.

Why? one wonders. Is it still there? And who dares look anyway? And what was so wise about it? I suppose she might have thought it would have a certain tourist value for the village in later centuries, but frankly I can't imagine anyone wanting to visit Waterley Cross, with or without the attraction of finding a deadly, or even dead spider. I am certainly not including it in this guide, other than in *en passant* mode, so I suggest you save your time for more fascinating experiences closer to Ambridge.

No, I'm sorry to say that Mother Keech's disgraceful behaviour, though well-intentioned, showed her up to be nothing more than a rank amateur. She certainly did nothing to enhance the status of witches in the area and it is probably all her fault that Waterley Cross is the way it is today.

On the positive side, she *is* known to have been one of Borsetshire's earliest doll collectors. Many witches used to people their lonely hovels with little waxen figures to keep them company, along with all their unusual live-stock. Of course, their curious habit of sticking pins into these 'poppets', as they were called, is said to pertain to putting spells on certain people, and causing pains with each prick. As a doll collector myself, I find it hard to believe that a witch would want to handle her delicate, waxen poppet so roughly, though I could understand her occasionally recycling one as a candle in an emergency. But I want to make it quite clear that, apart from a careful flick with a feather duster, my dolls remain undisturbed, and undis-turbing.

I was suddenly overwhelmed by a sense of *déjà vu*, perhaps because the reading room of Borchester Library was becoming too familiar. I looked at the pile of reference books in front of me; I gazed through the grimy windows at Underwoods across the road; I listened to the stertorous breathing of Baggy and Snatch as they dozed over the *Sun* by the radiator, and I knew that I needed a break, at least from the malodorous presence of B&S, though I made a mental note to interview them later. Was I getting too deeply enmeshed in this whole supernatural revelation, and where was it leading?

Well, I can tell you. It led me to Tom Forrest, who I've always considered a sensible man of the woods. I briefed him on my discoveries thus far while standing in a leafy glade in Leader's Wood, and at my mention of witches, he chuckled knowingly.

'Well, Mrs Snell, you're standing under a witch tree right now.' Startled, I looked up to see a rather beautiful and quite innocent-looking oak.

'This is a cork oak,' he continued, 'and witches used to grow these in secret, to extract the brown cork stain from the bark. Then, if they had to go through the water test, they covered themselves in the cork stain to aid buoy-ancy and hopefully prove their innocence.'

I tactfully informed him that he'd got it completely wrong and that, according to my research, it was the other way round – to float was supposed to be a sign of guilt. He seemed quite unperturbed by this discovery and

conveniently shrugged it off with a total *non sequitur.*

'Ah well, I reckon they musta thought, "What's the good of being inno-cent if I'm expected to drown anyway. At least if I can float a bit, I got a chance of making a getaway."'

Thoroughly confused, I tried to make *my* getaway, but it was not to be.

'Hang on, I've just remembered summat. You've got a witch in your garden at the Hall, y'know.'

I was shocked, but gripped.

'Yeah, Molly the Witch. Now *she* spread herself about, and no mistake!'

Even more shocked, I demanded to know just what *exactly* he was getting at!

'Well, y'know that bed of yellow peonies you got down by the river? Well, their Latin name is Peony Mollokovitchy. Huh! self-respecting country folk could never get their tongues round summat like that, so they're allus known as Molly the Witch. And they also has a habit of seeding theirselves allover the place, and what's more, peonies don't normally like damp soil, they prefer a dry, chalky spot. So I reckon you got a real magical mystery there alright!'

He was right. I rushed to my *Great Plants Of Our Time* by Daphne Hyde-Wooddew and thumbed through to find '*Paeonia mlokosewitschii* – young

Molly the Witch making her triumphant getaway by broomstick.

plum-coloured shoots emerge in spring, developing into soft green leaves with a hint of copper. Exquisite cool yellow flowers; likes good drainage and tolerates chalk.'

So, why was Molly the Witch growing so happily in the marshy land of the river garden? Could she have been involved in the dreaded water test, and was she 'the one that got away', according to Tom Forrest's theory?

Things were really hotting up and getting much closer to home than I had thought possible. So many factors were falling into place: I am a dedicated plant lover; I have always been sensitive to country matters and the need to preserve our wild flora and fauna; I have, for some time, written a problem page for the *Ambridge Village Voice* and so can rightfully claim an affinity with those bygone agony aunts.

It seemed that there was only one conclusion to be drawn: Could Molly have left her spirit in the 'soul memory' of the yellow paeonies, safe in the garden of Ambridge Hall, knowing that one day, centuries later, a fellow sympathiser would be living there? And, more to the point, could I, Lynda

Not quite how I see myself as a witch.

Snell, be the reincarnation of Molly, and (QED) – a witch?

Weak with the burden of such a revelation, I rushed into the house to lie down in a darkened room (the Beige Boudoir, actually, on my authentic French *bateau lit*. Such a pity Robert has never felt comfortable with it, claiming that it gives him *mal de mer*, but I've always loved its decadent state-ment.). My thoughts were coalescing at a rate of knots, among them Joe Grundy's portentous words, '*The Cat and Fiddle!* Eh? Think about it, Missus!' This, coupled with my earlier sighting of Baggy and Snatch in the reading room, seemed significant since they practically lived in the car park of that notorious hostelry, and would doubtless have some well-informed opinions of the place.

My next problem was to arrange a meeting in a venue from which B&S had not already been banned. I considered the Workman's Cafe at the back of Underwoods as a possibility, then remembered that, in less-happy times, I myself had once secretly rendezvoused there with a private detective; no point in awakening bad memories, I decided.

That only left the reading room where they were still allowed access, on educational grounds only, but since the likelihood of them creating noisy, embarrassing scenes there might result in *my* being banned, I agreed to meet them by the bottle bank in the Cat & Fiddle car park at dusk, just before opening time.

I arrived promptly and waited for five minutes. Nothing! Then I heard strange sounds from the depths of the bottle bank, and watched transfixed as two ghostly apparitions levered themselves out, clutching a seeming cocktail of sundry dregs.

'Evenin', Missus! – Hic! – You're early!'

'What are you doing in that bottle bank, Baggy?'

'Oh, er, just doin' a bit of re-cycling, like!'

'I see. Well, can we please get on with our interview – I don't want to be seen loitering around here much longer.'

I proceeded to fill them in on JG's cryptic challenge plus some selected highlights from my research.

'Aar, I thought I seen you sleeping it off behind a pile of books in the readin' room, Missus. Well, whaddya wanna know?'

'How dare you, Snatch, I was *reading* those books! Now, can you tell me why the Cat & Fiddle is so-called and is it connected with witchcraft in the area?'

Baggy immediately produced a grimy palm, 'What's it worth, then Missus?' (Oh dear!)

'We'll settle for an IOU for a pint of Shires and a meat pie each.'

Talking to Baggy gave me nightmares.

I complied, comforted to know that at least they were observing what I knew to be the going rate. After a couple a swigs on his current bottle, 'To oil me wezand, like' (local dialect for 'to lubricate one's vocal chords'), Baggy commenced thus:

'Well, it hath been said … Hic!'

'Yes, yes go on. It hath been said … what?'

'Well, that's it.'

'What do you mean? I thought you said …'

'It hath been said as how, once upon a time, Molly the Witch [Oh no!] was landlady of this inn and, like all witches, she had a cat. And one night, the juke-box packed up, so she invited her ol' mate the Devil to come over an' give 'em all a tune on 'is fiddle. Well, just then, the 'Ob 'Ound come a-gallopin' in, sees the cat and chases after it, and all hell breaks out! The Devil and Molly follow in hot pursuit and they all end up in the village pond drownded and are never seen again.'

'Is that it?'

'Yep. Right, it's gone opening time, so …'

'Excuse me, excuse me, er, do you know if they went via the garden at Ambridge Hall?'

'Why should they wanna do that?'

'Oh, no matter. So are you saying that that's why the pub is called the Cat and Fiddle?'

'Yep. Cheerio then, Missus.'

As I watched them staggering pub-wards, I had the uncomfortable feeling that this was, in fact, a set-up contrived by JG and B&S, presumably to throw me off the scent. But, in fact, they had inadvertently answered the question that had been haunting me – Was I a witch?

Answer: Well, no, of course not, and for one very good reason – I am not now, and never have been, a cat person. And it is common knowledge that witches always have cats as familiars to aid in their contact with the occult. What is more, I've always considered cats devious and untrustworthy, with good reason it seems, and feel much more comfortable with dogs, with the exception of the Hob Hound, of course.

As I returned to the Hall, I felt strangely comforted by all that I had discovered. I ventured down to the Am, hoping for a glimpse of Molly's paeonies gleaming lucently in the lingering afterglow. And indeed, there they were, reminding me that even though it seemed that I was not destined to venture further along the Mystical Path, perhaps I had at least been granted the privilege of playing host to the secret memory of Molly the Witch, the 'one that got away'.

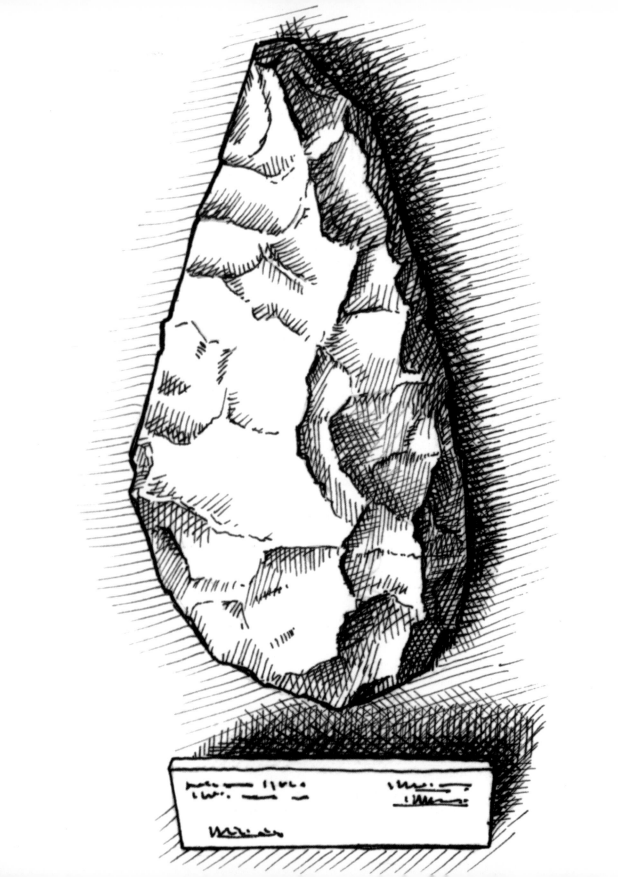

Feudin', Fussin' & A-Fightin'

Great, and sometimes inspirational, campaigns and Great Village Rows

The perceptive visitor to Ambridge will soon realise that so charming a spot is unlikely to have evolved over the centuries without the odd clash of opinions. Indeed, it has been said that Ambridge is a nice, safe place with a violent history. How true those words are, even today!

Surely the fact that a Neolithic axe was found as close to home as the grounds of Ambridge Hall in 1893 – hastily removed to Borchester Museum where it is still viewable, by appointment only – proves that some kind of weaponry was deemed necessary by our earliest forefathers, and leads one to wonder if there might have been a surviving skull into which that axe was embedded. We shall probably never know.

Of course, a pacifist's view might be that an axe could quite as easily have been used for chopping down trees for shelter or kindling, or for hunting animals for supper – perfectly acceptable behaviour, considering the rather primitive circumstances.

All I'm saying is that if it's worth having, it's worth fighting for! Which is why, since arriving in Ambridge, I have deemed it my responsibility to lead

Neolithic axe on view in Borchester Museum. I leave you to imagine whose skull it might have made contact with.

campaigns, missions – whatever – in order to right all manner of rural wrongs, which would surely remain unaddressed, but for my commitment and determination.

And while not always approving of the often warlike motives, I must confess that I have taken inspiration from some of the following campaigns which litter Ambridge's history.

In considering the more contentious side of life in this peaceful village, we must start as far back as the Romans who, having crossed the Fosse Way and subdued the tribes of Borsetshire (loosely known as the Borsings), settled down to the relatively peaceful occupation of leaving bits of pottery lying around all over the place for all *sorts* of people to find aeons later. I'm sure they intended nothing more than a quite natural desire to be remembered as gentle artisans, as well as ruthless conquerors, but frankly, their random behaviour amounts to something approaching wanton carelessness!

In fact, the amount of confusion, bordering on outrage, every time a villager finds a shard of so-called Roman pottery has to be seen to be believed. I myself have not escaped the annoyance of farmers like Phil Archer, who take a quite irrational exception to my discreet inspection of their land at ploughing time or whenever a new building project is in hand. And I have to say, the scepticism which greets one's discovery of some interesting artefact (even if it is difficult to authenticate, and *does* usually turn out to be a chunk of drainage pipe) is very undermining.

The Borsings were simple country-dwellers, who tilled the land and pursued a relatively peaceful lifestyle.

But, to continue, the next-known strife in the land was caused by the Normans, of course, and I'm quite sure their greatest obstacle was trying to get the locals to learn French, if my own experiments in this department are anything to go by.

I often ask myself, is it obstinacy, fear, sloth or xenophobia which seems to paralyse the Borsetshire brain when offered the opportunity to learn so gracious and elegant a language as French? I know it's easy for a bilingual like myself to assume that everyone has one's own flair and ear, but when I offered to give French lessons to those villagers keen to visit our twin French town of Meyruelle the apathy was ... well, *incroyable* doesn't really begin to describe it. Of course, an innate reluctance to part with money, and I don't think a mere £5 a lesson is unreasonable, is another disappointing rural trait

An odd Ambridge troubadour.

to be reckoned with in this whole sorry episode. Fortunately, physical violence never became part of the equation, so one can be thankful that Ambridge has made some cultural progress since the Normans.

But onwards, in our chronological review of Ambridge's tumultuous history, to what is, for a seasoned campaigner like myself, the most inspirational mission of all – the Crusades.

I'm not actually sure if any knights from Borsetshire sallied forth to fight in those noble engagements – it was a bit late in the day for Sir Launcelot du Lakey Hill – but there were likely to have been several yeomen from among the four great Ambridge families, not to mention the one from Chaucer's *Canterbury Tales*, 'A Christophere on his brest of silver sheen'. Who knows, maybe even the odd Ambridge troubadour – one of the few to pick up some phrase-book Norman French from a great-grandfather – was on hand to keep up the men's morale with a love ballad about their ladies fair (some of whom would be languishing at their spinning wheels in the great castle tower while others would be mending their filthy rags in the gloom of a muddy hovel – depending on rank).

The more well-born ladies of Borsetshire left to their own devices, while their menfolk ennobled themselves in the Crusades.

Which brings me, not surprisingly, to the Hundred Years War. I'm afraid it is one of those immovable objects which burdens many of us in-depth researchers – but so be it, in the cause of truth. And anyway, it has a particular significance at this point in time, since it was background to, and possible encourager of, the first Great Village Row (GVR) between the Archers/Fletchers and the Grundys. I have decided that this merits special attention in the chapter on the Great Families of Ambridge (please cross-refer yourselves).

The institution of the GVR was undoubtedly a major landmark in Ambridge social history giving, as it did, a precedent for every

kind of dispute between villagers ever since. I did search for evidence that the Bard may have sourced the GVR between the Montagues and Capulets in *Romeo and Juliet* from the current Ambridge GVR of the time. But to no avail – even though Ambridge was right on his doorstep. But then, as we know, great literature is probably paved with wasted opportunities!

Moving on to the Civil War – the source of much serious discord in and around Ambridge. The Battle of Hassett Bridge, as elsewhere documented in these pages (please refer to 'The Great Families of Ambridge'), conveys much of the tone of people's behaviour at the time, but has unexpected resonance, even today.

Ironic, is it not, that the suffering and heroism of those bloodthirsty times should today, have engendered two groups – the English Civil War Society and the Sealed Knot – dedicated to re-enacting scenes of historical carnage and mayhem in a caring and constructive way. (At least, that's how they see it. Personally, I can't help feeling that those elaborate costumes could be displayed to much greater effect and artistry, in a production of a Restoration comedy like Wycherley's *The Country Wife*. I see Clarrie Grundy as obvious casting for the title role – I don't think she's ready for anything too challenging just yet, despite her experience on celluloid).

And so, you may be fortunate enough to witness Dr Locke and his chums, acccoutred either in feathers and furbelows, or iron helmets – depending on how PC they're feeling and on who drew the short straw – cavorting about on horseback, and churning a perfectly good field into a disgusting quagmire.

Or you may prefer, in the elegant comfort of your room at Grey Gables, to watch my video, *Ambridge – a Village at War*, filmed at considerable personal risk in the heat of battle (with children's costumes made by myself and the odd village seamstress) and available at Reception to rent or buy.

I feel that, at this moment in time, it might be helpful to the visitor to say that I am well aware that I am not the first or only campaigner in Ambridge's history

The Battle of Hassett Bridge.

to answer the challenge, 'He who would be valiant be, let him come within', but I think that what distinguishes me from the rest is that I observe some simple rules on the subject. One main ingredient of the campaign spirit is to remain calm and keep a balanced perspective at all times, since things can so easily get out of hand if enthusiasm waxes too great. I'm afraid this is often the reason for an honourable campaign developing into a full-blown GVR before you know what's hit you – usually a large, solid object in those days. What now follows illustrates this phenomenon in every way, regrettably.

GVRs continued to rumble on all through the next century. But it was in 1793 that, for me, the most interesting socio-exotic interaction took place – interesting, because it was positively eccentric.

Lord Netherbourne. (Can you see his tragic flaw?)

Yes, we're talking about the French Revolution, the Reign of Terror, when hundreds of French aristos were desperately trying to flee Madame Guillotine, huddled on draughty cross-channel *paquets* – later replaced by the much faster and more comfortable ferries, so beloved today by Francophiles, gourmets and Morris Men on one-day shopping trips.

Their hope was for sanctuary in England as guests of the sympathetic aristocracy and, indeed, it was one of the few French-speaking gentry in Borsetshire, Lord Netherbourne (an ancestor of Caroline Pemberton's, incidentally, and I'm sure she'd be happy to chat to you about him if you catch her in Reception), who initiated our next Ambridge Campaign, to 'Rescue an Emigré'.

What is not clear is how he intended to involve the community in this noble venture. I put the question to Caroline, who suggested that he probably tried the 'Dunkirk little ships method' – carefully selected Ambridge villagers picking up the emigrés in rowing boats, from somewhere in the Solent, and smuggling them inland from Buckler's Hard on the Beaulieu River, avoiding the revolutionary spies who lurked everywhere.

The Grundys reception of the émigrés was hostile and typically unsophisticated.

I didn't like to say that I thought this sounded rather impractical, and not what I had in mind at all – after all, Lord Netherbourne was Caroline's relation and she might think it rather impertinent of me to disagree with her version of family folklore. I also considered it too delicate to mention that she was missing the point – again, her tragic flaw at work, I'm afraid.

But, in the scheme of things, my reservations were all academic because, as one might expect, the Grundys managed to sabotage even this early example of humanitarian foreign aid with cries of:

'Hang on, we got enough bloody gentry already, ta very much. We don't want no more, do we?'

And, having persuaded the villagers in their own inimitable way that fancy foreign aristocracy was even worse than the home-grown variety, they managed to raise their own revolution against Lord Netherbourne, who was only trying to do the decent thing as I'm sure Caroline will agree.

Imagine how those poor, bedraggled Frenchmen and women must have felt, having just escaped from one howling mob only to be confronted by another, Grundy-led, blocking the Lower Loxley Road and all wearing bizarre-looking bunches of dog-roses, thistles and leeks (presumably their crude nationalistic answer to the French Tricolour) and shouting, 'Push off back home, bloody Frogs!'

But the ingenious émigrés, fired by their late Queen Marie Antoinette's defiant cry of 'Let them eat cake!', had sensibly concealed in their *portmanteaux* some delicious specimens of *tarte aux pommes, roulade au chocolat* and *Iles flottantes*, which they hurled at the screaming peasant hordes who, perforce, surrendered their taste-buds, and themselves, to a hedonistic orgy of delight.

This resulted in an outright *coup de grace* (or even a *coupe royale!*) for the French, who felt it was a far, far better thing to make for the Channel Islands as soon as the coast was clear, and a fairly dishonourable defeat for the Grundys, who, *comme d'habitude*, blamed the Archer Curse for the whole demeaning debacle.

Another GVR, which is less well-chronicled, is the Great Compost Scandal of 1873. This was all due to the habit of farmers building large compost heaps against the walls of their stone barns, presumably to aid stability in high winds and to speed up the rotting process. Unfortunately, this seemingly sound ecological practice led to numerous cases of spontaneous combustion inside the heap and many barns were burnt to a pile of rubble.

Word of this spread as far as the Yorkshire Dales where a series of unusually mild winters had preserved the vast network of traditional stone wall field boundaries in good condition, resulting in serious unemployment among the dry-stone walling community.

Understandably, the dry-stone wallers got on their bikes and headed south to look for work in Borsetshire and, finding plenty of material lying around the ruined barns, they offered their services to the less scrupulous landowners, and built walls in all the wrong places, so that field boundaries were altered in favour of the landowner.

A huge GVR broke out between the landowners and the tenant farmers, which soon escalated into a campaign by the local hedgers and ditchers, who naturally saw their livelihoods threatened by these incomers. Eventually, the dry-stone wallers were driven out of the village – a great loss to the community when one thinks how the introduction of Yorkshire cheesecake, Yorkshire pudding and barm cakes might have invigorated local cuisine. As it was, they came and they went, and today the only remaining vestige of a dry-stone wall is the strange hummock in Clarrie Grundy's garden which she refers to as her rockery. She tells me it 'evolved', and in a way, I think she's right – it certainly doesn't look as though it's had the benefit of Man's influence, in fact, some might say Mother Nature has outstayed her welcome. But at least the visitor to Ambridge, already advised by me to avoid Grange Farm for aesthetic reasons, will be spared the spectacle, and Clarrie knows I've offered to redesign the whole nebulous plot for her at no charge, so maybe, some day . . . I will say no more!

Of course, some years ago, Tom Forrest conducted his own personal GVR against the then vicar, whose anti-hunting sermons had pointed a denouncing finger at Tom's profession of gamekeeping. Naturally a proud man, Tom was very bitter, especially since the Vicar had often accepted the odd brace of pheasant from him, and so decided to boycott the church, taking half the congregation with him.

It was a formidable impasse, but I'm glad to say the Christian spirit won through and the vicar finally offered a grudging apology, if only to re-unite his riven flock (as good a reason as any), and another GVR abated. I'm not sure if Tom was completely appeased. Where church matters are concerned, one feels it never takes much to upset him, as was evidenced by his somewhat churlish approach to the subject of women priests. But I don't intend to permit even the rumble of a GVR on that subject.

No, I think I can say confidently that under my guidance, serious GVRs are a thing of the past. But campaigns are, of course, another matter.

Surprisingly, even before I arrived in Ambridge, the villagers had attempted a number of campaigns, with varying degrees of success, including to: (1) establish a network of cycle paths after the closure of the local train line; (2) stop cruelty to animals in Borchester market, as well as in factory farms; (3) object to the erection of pylons, and get representation on the district council.

Smiling 'valiantly' in the thick of a campaign.

All very worthy in their way, too. But I have to say that, while they may have scored Alpha+ for enthusiasm and energy, they were still on a learning curve when it came to leadership.

Thus it was that with the fresh, detached perception of, yes, an incomer, I was able to spot deficiencies and swiftly calculate priorities within my game-plan strategy.

From the outset, I knew my biggest problem would be the farmers and their cohorts – but then, how to change the attitudes of those who are congenitally stubborn and indifferent to more enlightened approaches has always been my brief, ever since Sunningdale.

Leader's Wood – a favourite conservation spot of mine.

In this instance, I went on a one-week intensive farming course to gain an in-depth overview of all aspects of groundroots farming, plus a psychological profile on what makes farmers tick.

I have never regretted this step – it has served me well throughout numerous confrontations, run-ins, stand-offs, one-to-ones and hands-on experiences with the likes of Tony Archer, David Archer, Brian Aldridge, Mike Tucker *et al.*, and I think I can honestly say that I am known and respected for my fair and frank opinions on just about everything rural from rabbits to ragwort.

And so it is that, nowadays, the visitor strolls around Ambridge and its environs, and takes for granted the ancient oak trees that I saved from Mike Tucker's axe with a preservation order, or the rare, and similarly threatened, Wild Service Tree I found in Leader's Wood. This resulted in the awarding of an SSSI (Site of Special Scientific Interest) and those don't grow on trees, I can tell you!

Similarly, the footpaths along which you stroll, the country pond on Home Farm territory and the red phone box outside the shop are still in existence only because I fought, with the occasional aid of a Happy Few, to overcome the intransigence of farmers and other anti-conservationists. (Sadly, since Martha died, the plastic flowers in the phone box require more 'pruning' – that is, washing, dusting and replacing. Shula is quietly dutiful about this, as am I, when I remember.) Future footpath-foraging will include tracing the underwater track which I am convinced runs beneath Arkwright Lake in the grounds of Grey Gables. I'm hoping to persuade Mr Woolley that dredging and draining operations may be necessary, and if I can commandeer a village working party to keep down the cost, I don't foresee a problem: it will be such an ecological coup – after all, how many entrepreneurs can claim to have a public right of way through the middle of their lake?

And it doesn't stop there – the list goes on. Thanks to my tireless petitioning:

1. We do *not* have a feeder road to the Borchester bypass violating the peace of Ambridge.
2. We *do* have a rare hawk, a Montagu's harrier, nesting undisturbed by David Archer's crop sprayer.
3. We have hedgehogs saved from the bonfire (in conjunction with St Tiggywinkle's Animal Hospital), many of whom are happily eating pellet-free slugs thanks to my Green tract on the horrors of metaldihyde.

Happy hedgehog snuggling down for the winter.

4. Visitors can find their way easily around the area with the aid of original wooden finger posts, saved from demolition by my campaign HOOF (Hands Off Our Finger Posts). This vital piece of Ambridge heritage also removes the embarrassing need to ask directions of locals, who can be both unhelpful and unintelligible, 'if they'm a mind ter be.'
5. We have ancient hedgerows, unvandalised by David Archer's (yes, ITMA, I'm afraid) digger. That was very stressful and involved my near immolation on the jaws of the dreadful apparatus. It was a close thing, in every sense, and without the eleventh-hour appearance of a BET (Borsetshire Environment Trust) representative I don't think I'd have made it. All ended well, though I predict that ancient hedges will remain a thorny issue in my future entanglements over conservation – I haven't forgotten my commitment to Aethelwold's Hedge or Edric's Ditch. (Cross-refer to 'Great Families'.)

6. We still have a village hall which is in a fit state of repair, and hopefully meets EU regulations, only because I invited Anneka Rice to help us rally the village to work as a team on refurbishing the building.

Hedgerows (particularly if they are ancient) provide vital habitat for many species of bird.

7. Traffic-calming has come to Ambridge! I think I reached nirvana with this one. There was a wonderful sense of village unity and the sight of people turning out uncomplainingly in all weathers to count the passing vehicles and painstakingly record their speeds was most rewarding. It's true that there were times when I despaired of Betty's maths and Clarrie's punctuality, but it only took a little imagination for the figures to look convincing on paper. And the heady challenge of standing in the middle of the road, braving the oncoming lorries and camper vans, *compelling* them to slow down, was reminiscent of how the suffragettes must have felt when chained to the railings. Except that, perhaps, in a way – it wasn't.

Anneka and I prepare to go to work..

Of course, achieving 'Slow Down' signs at each of the main roads into Ambridge was the impossible dream come true. How sad for the visitor that it was destined to become a nightmare, when these very signs disappeared suddenly without anyone having the courtesy to tell me, their instigator. But I remain undaunted. Those signs were meant to be, and they will return – I am trawling the Internet regularly for possible sitings in rival villages around the country, and I'm sure the thief is hoping that no dreadful accidents occur as a result of his/her despicable behaviour!

I have toyed with the idea of including the unpleasantness between Laurence Lovell and myself over his so-called production of *Cinderella* in this collection of campaigns and GVRs. I have decided not to for two reasons: firstly, I do not wish to be accused of dishonesty by granting such status to what was little more than a flagrant display of artistic inadequacy on his part and, secondly, the whole sordid business is dealt with fully in my chapter on the Arts, 'Poet and Peasant'.

But I cannot contemplate leaving the crucial subject of GVRs without mentioning the delicate matter of the Best Kept Village competition. Now I wish to say, categorically, that I regard this time-honoured institution as an inspired way of maintaining village morale, but I do not believe it should be a 'Nimby's Charter' for bending the genuine countryside into a blueprint for smug suburbanites and a new breed of Aga louts. (Robert says he doesn't

These well-kept cottages are my blue-print for Ambridge – the proprietors should be congratulated for maintaining a pleasing balance between indivuality and order.

understand a word of the above, and anyway, he loves our Aga and wouldn't dream of kicking it or pouring beer over it!)

I think what I'm saying is that while this competition encourages people to take pride in their properties and gardens, it can lead to extremes of behaviour (from incomers and locals alike) bordering on the seriously dysfunctional. Not that I have any objection to white-washing stones along the roadside (a habit of the late Walter Gabriel's, I believe – it's attractive and keeps the tractors in their place. And I'm a great advocate of sweet-smelling, flower-bedecked telephone boxes enhancing our living heritage, as was the case of Martha Woodford's.

But the wholesale gang-mowing of wildflower verges by over-enthusiastic families of yuppie incomers, in the cause of style and presentation, smacks of the boardroom. Personally, I find it infuriating because it makes dreadful inroads on my supply of nutritious nettles, thus depleting our already limited food resources, and I know for a fact that the Council for the Protection of Rural England is very worried about it, judging by a sound byte of theirs: 'Over-zealous tidiness has no place in English villages in our view' – or in mine either, actually!

Fortunately, by monitoring people's behaviour with my video on Ambridge village life – a sort of fly-on-the-wall documentary – I succeeded in highlighting a somewhat casual attitude to tidiness and litter. I'm afraid I had to make an example of someone in a desperate attempt to get my message across, so I chose Peggy Woolley and the dropped box of eggs. But any number of villagers might have qualified, especially those who were so reluctant to help me dredge the disgustingly polluted village pond (see 'Village Walkabout' for details).

I did not foresee what seething emotions and blind fury my innocent exposé that night at the public viewing in the village hall, would engender, particularly from Jill Archer who leapt to Peggy Woolley's defence with all guns blazing. I must say, I felt routed, not to say humiliated, by the experience, and I think a major GVR was only narrowly avoided.

But it only goes to prove my point that from little seed potatoes, mighty GVRs can grow.

It has been said that life in a village is really a microcosm of life all over the country, so it's hardly surprising that however petty the issue may seem to the outsider, the potential for undercurrents and hidden agendas must be understood.

Let us then gaze with new insight at this peaceful village, never forgetting the often bloody endeavours of those inhabitants, past and present, to make it the safe and desirable place we see today.

Upstairs Downstairs

Manners, modes & morals through the ages

You visitors to Ambridge who come from an urban background, where class boundaries have been largely eroded and status often depends solely on the size of one's web-site or how often one changes one's car, where the fast pace of life has replaced the vocabulary of courtesy with a vocal shorthand of grunts and shrugs (few of them Gallic, either), where time taken to stand and stare might be misconstrued as sussing the joint prior to a heist – you might wonder at the high, if somewhat old-fashioned, standard of social intercourse in and around Ambridge.

Yes, people *will* still greet you with a cheery 'Good morning' or 'Good afternoon', and who knows, if you stick around long enough, you might be honoured with an 'And what brings you here?' – but I don't hold out much hope.

Personally, I favour a well-projected 'Coo-eee!'– particularly useful when toiling across dank fields trying to attract the attention of people like Debbie Aldridge or Ruth Archer. I find it usually stops them in their tracks, at least long enough for me to have my say on whatever important enterprise has current priority on my hit list.

I suppose it's their youthful energy that enables them to hurtle off to their own, more mundane pursuits with such alacrity, often before I've even finished speaking. But I feel sure this is more likely to be due to Short-Attention-Span Syndrome (something I encounter daily in my endeavours) than to bad manners, so I make the usual allowances.

Drinking tea is one English pastime that transcends class.

Indeed, such can be the bonhomie of certain members of the community as to leave one quite overwhelmed. I shall never forget the day, soon after Robert and I had moved into the Hall, when Tom Forrest arrived on the doorstep with a brace of rabbits – ungutted and unskinned – as a welcoming present. I was just about to say, 'Take those disgusting things outside, they're dripping all over the quarry tiles, and anyway, I don't think we've been introduced!' when some instinct – I don't know what it was – made me stop and ask myself, 'Could this be some ancient country custom, or even initiation ceremony, that it would be only proper to engage with?'

Well, I never did discover the truth about it because, just then, Eddie Grundy appeared as if from thin air and said, 'Ere, Missis, you give 'em to me, you don't want ter get your fair hands into that lot – I'll get my Clarrie to paunch 'em for yer; she'll do it for a tenner, no problem!'

And so it was that I had my first encounter with two of the most native sons of Ambridge soil, as they encouraged me to perform that ancient country tradition of handing over money. At the time, I was only too glad to get rid of Tom, Eddie and the rabbits, but later, with hindsight, I realised my instinct had been right, and it was their simple, rustic way of saying, 'Welcome, Missis. You be one of us now.'

Certainly, Eddie has continued to pursue the money-exchanging custom at every opportunity, though not always in order to make me feel at home, I fear, while Tom prefers the bartering method via the odd bit of rural wisdom or jar of home-made jam in return for the odd lift up to Brookfield or Home Farm, or advice on his campaign for a kissing gate (not that I was much help to him on that, having matters of greater moment in hand at the time).

So, in what is this relatively civilised social interaction grounded? Is it specific to Ambridge or would you find Felpersham friendliness as favourable? Is Borchester more boorish or Hollerton huffier?

These were all questions I attempted to put to passers-by in a recent survey I conducted while trapped inside the revolving doors of Underwoods. It was a surreal experience, though not without literary merit as I, alone, remained poised, like T.S. Eliot, at the 'still centre of the turning world', surrounded by a whirling mass of arms and legs all trying to escape either in or out of the store.

Pointless to explain the multiple-choice options on my questionnaire to people suffering from the effects of vertigo and claustrophobia, and impossible to extract a constructive opinion from anyone. Sadly, I have to admit the exercise was not a success, and the overall reaction was one of awesome apathy tinged with some rather aggressive vocal negativity, which made me doubt the point of investigating *politesse* at all.

From one end of the social scale to the other; the serf must toil in the field while his feudal overlord enjoys a musical interlude in the garden.

Therefore, the conclusion I have decided to draw is that, in a heritage context, Borsetshire courtesy derives from feudal times, when knights, barons and lords of the manor ruled the land and deference, as well as hefty tithes, had to be paid on a regular basis, often on pain of death.

So the habit of cap-doffing and forelock-tugging was *de rigueur*, if the average serf wanted to survive the demands of his feudal lord. And of course, the time spent on these routine gestures of servility meant less time for hard toil in the fields, which nobody minded, so life was set at a comfortable walking pace – except when there was war, pillaging or plague in progress.

Paradoxically, today, Joe Grundy's cap remains rooted to his pate in deference to nobody, enabling him to spend the time saved in downing twice as many pints of Shires as his peers who might be trying to maintain high standards of behaviour. But once one accepts that Joe is the exception to most rules, the whole thing falls into perspective and there's absolutely no need to fret about it.

Though the pace of life in Ambridge may have speeded up somewhat from those distant times – under the influence of progress and technology – it is still slower than the mindless rat race of urban living – thanks largely to the vigilance and careful monitoring of people like myself.

Indeed, it is often those same townies, as I affectionately call them (in private, and only in front of Robert), who, returning from a stroll around the village, usually including a stop at the Bull, lean on my reception desk and pose the age-old conundrum, 'Lynda, love, can you tell me the SP on something that's been doing my head in? Can you tell me why it is that some people round here get the old full-title treatment and others, like your good self, seem to be down for more of a first-name job?' I have to say that these guests are often businessmen whose expenses make them rather expansive, but I never allow that sort of familiarity to upset me, if only for the sake of good PR, and I have no objection to answering a friendly enquiry.

The problem is that there is no easy way to explain the complex, often illogical rules which apply to this subject, shrouded as it is in an unspoken mystique that has puzzled countless generations of townies and rustics alike. My own rules, based on the observations of a whole decade of country living, are thus: (a) to anyone I consider to be my social equal, I grant the familiarity of first name-terms – on a *mutual* basis. These would include the following: Jill, Jennifer, Marjorie, Nelson and the late Guy (Pemberton); (b) to those of a less . . . sophisticated background, I prefer to use the first-name form – but would expect *them* to address *me* as Mrs Snell. These would include Bert (Fry), Joe (Grundy) and Tom (Forrest).

Naturally, in the event of my being less than pleased with one of the above mentioned, I make a point of using their full title: 'What a pity you didn't tell me you were colluding with Hayley over the script for *Cinderella*, Mr Fry!'; 'Call yourself an author, do you, *Jennifer Aldridge*? You're nothing but a cheap hack!' (I've never actually said that to her, but I've often thought about it, so I think it's quite a useful example.)

This measure, I've noticed, rarely makes any immediate difference to the offender's behaviour, but one must always hope that it may eventually impact on them in some positive way at a later date.

Then there are special cases, like Susan Carter, who is permitted to call me 'Lynda' as part of a subtle social development programme which began when I offered her a glass of sherry. She is making progress but is somewhat handicapped by Neil, who doesn't share her aspirations. But I've told her to be patient, and I think she will be – it *is* the only way.

Which brings me to my rather equivocal relationship with Jack and Peggy Woolley. I entered into my role on Reception at Grey Gables fully aware of the social implications and foreseeing no problems – on my side, at least. Unfortunately, Peggy Woolley seemed to find that our existing first-name relationship was no longer appropriate between employer and employee, and insisted that I should address both her and her husband formally.

It was soon after this that she had me demoted from Receptionist to chambermaid – obviously part of the same ploy – need I say more?

But back to feudal resonance for a moment. You will always hear Bert Fry refer to Phil Archer as 'Boss', a traditional title, used with affection rather than subservience. And of course, the ubiquitous 'Missis' or 'Missus' is a wonderful, all-purpose way of overcoming the problem of formal or informal address – but perhaps only if you are of a rustic persuasion.

So, to sum up for the visitor, I would recommend that you simply avoid direct conversation with anyone unless and until you are formally introduced, when I suggest you address them as 'Sir' while endeavouring to speak with a heavy foreign accent – Dutch is always good – so that they will think your English is limited and will make the usual allowances!

And so, having established the importance of social status, let us examine its post-feudal, post-modern significance.

It is a well-known fact that feudalism still existed in Ambridge in the mid-1950s in the shape of the Lawson-Hope family, who had been seated at the Manor (now the residence of a retired businessman) since the tenth century – with a family coat of arms to prove it.

The Lawson-Hope coat of arms. I'm happy to note these swords are not crossed.

Many Ambridge inhabitants worked for the Lawson-Hopes over the years, including Doris Archer who started out as a humble scullery wench and was later promoted to lady's maid/PA to Lady Lettie Lawson-Hope herself. How, I wonder, would she have coped with the stinging humiliation that I had to endure when I was demoted from Receptionist to chambermaid? At least her progress was in the right direction. So much for social enlightenment! Or perhaps I should be thankful that today's scullery wenches come from a catering agency in Borchester and consist mainly of Antipodean students backpacking their way through British, and any other heritage they can fit in to their holiday visa limits.

And how ironic it is that, with the caring, if paternalistic, attitude of the aristocracy, Lady Lettie, as a token of gratitude, bequeathed the charming Glebe Cottage to Doris who sensibly let it to Ned Larkin, a Brookfield farm labourer, and finally bequeathed it to Shula, her granddaughter. Sadly, such appreciative gestures from employer to employee rarely pertain today, and I have no illusions that Peggy Woolley is planning to leave The Lodge to me in her will. And if she did, that electronic cat-flap would be the first thing to go, I can assure you!

But in those days, there were many long-standing customs involving the squire and/or his wife administering benefice to their workers. For example, the squire's wife would always bring the Caundle – a mixture of oatmeal, sugar and ale – to a newly delivered mother, as a nourishing pick-me-up. Surprisingly, some mothers were teetotal, even in those days before antenatal advice about not drinking during pregnancy – or maybe they simply couldn't face the thought of a pint of home brew – and so were given a Caundle mixed with water from the Caundle Well in Woodbine Cottage.

Another example of birthing beneficence was when the lady of the manor brought a gift of cakes to a new mother. What an occasion in the lives of these humble folk! Imagine the awe on their grubby faces as the gracious gentlewoman entered the lowly abode and presented her offering, elegantly arranged in a raffia gardening trug and covered with a chequered handkerchief. And picture the delight as they shyly bit into the delicacies – probably two dozen simple rock buns or drop scones, batch-baked by cook (anything more elaborate might have given the wrong impression), but enough to feed the family for a week.

Gratitude was usually expressed with a mumbled, 'Thank you, M'am' – they wouldn't have had the vocabulary for much more – and accompanied by suitable nods and curtseys. *Except*, of course, in the case of Doris Archer's mother, Lisa, who refused to 'Know her place', as was customary, and defied Lady Lettie's comments on the fact with, 'I bow my knee to God Almighty, and to God Almighty alone!'

But then, she *was* of yeoman farmer stock and considered herself a cut above the lowly cottagers who would eagerly prostrate themselves for a crumb.

And so the status saga goes on: even young Doris Forrest/Archer would have vied for a space at the sole, cracked mirror in the servants' quarters on Sunday mornings, to check her appearance, then off to church in her dark blue cloak and straw bonnet, trying to look superior to the other maids, all similarly dressed, and the footmen in their bright yellow, with silver buttons. Their employers provided this apparel, which was viewed as a mark of their status as well as their servants', but only the butler was allowed to wear his own clothes to church in view of his special position in the household.

Miserable peasants about to be cheered up by an enthusiastic Lady Lettie.

I'm sorry to say that one butler, a Mr Webber, rather foolishly abused this position by getting drunk at the village fete one year. He was led discreetly away from the scene to avoid further embarrassment, but you can imagine the colourful conversation downstairs that evening:

Scullery wench: Well, what about Mr Webber at the fete, then, eh?

Cook: What *about* Mr Webber? You just mind yer tongue, my girl, and stop yer shacklin' – there's work to be done!

Footman: She's right though, Mrs Widges – d'ye think he'll get the sack? He were all arsy versy with drink – they had a right sprunt to get him to calm down.

Young Doris: Well, I'm not surprised. I've often seen him taking a nip of Her Ladyship's sherry when she weren't looking, but I didn't dare say anything. He's tried to pither me a coupla times, an' all, but I weren't having none of his clawin' words. I told him, 'My Dan'll pikel you and shog the daylights out of yer, you keep this up.' He were that unked! I had to laugh!

Cook: Yes, alright, alright, young Doris – that's enough of that. There's Her Ladyship's bell – get moilin' this minute!

Of course, upstairs, the matter would not have been referred to until after breakfast the next morning, and in an altogether more comprehensible vocabulary.

Lady Lettie: My dear, have you considered the matter of Webber?

Squire: Hardly, my dear, I've been too busy discussing the rents with my bailiff. What had you in mind?

Lady Lettie: Well, as you know, my dear, I always leave such matters to you, but I have noticed that my sherry seems to be diminishing at an alarming rate. It couldn't possibly be young Doris, because I recently offered her a glass, quite deliberately, as part of her improvement, you know, and she turned her nose up at the taste. So disappointing!

Squire: Well, my dear, I'm not prepared to have a fuss. Webber's a good man. Knows his stuff. Fine army record and that sort of thing. I shall probably decide to overlook the matter, but, er, continue to keep an eye on the sherry for me, would you? There's a dear old thing. Lady Day is approaching, and the men have their expectations of one.

I often wish I had known the Lawson-Hopes. I think we would have had much in common and they epitomise such admirable qualities – a natural dignity and graciousness; sensitivity to the needs of those less fortunate; a desire to improve the state of the countryside – and not a snobbish thought in their heads. Which is what breeding is all about. And which Julia Pargetter should have remembered when dismissing me to 'other ranks' among the extras on *Isabella – An Orpahn Jilted*. After all airs and graces are somewhat *au dessuss de sa gare* when one's husband's name is Pargetter.

What she may not realise is that the name Pargetter has two meanings. The first, a 'plasterer or whitewasher' refers to the lost, ancient craft of 'pargetting' or ornamental plasterwork, used to cover the exterior walls of small houses and cottages in earlier times. So it is quite likely that her husband's family were in trade as skilled artisans and flourished for a time, though when the fashion died out they may well have resorted to painting and decorating.

But back to the squire's mention of Lady Day, which signifies one of the brief flashes of democracy shining through the unremitting gloom of serfdom. Yes, 25 March was the day the half-yearly rents were paid and the age-old country custom of handing over money (in a hessian bag this time) was performed. The squire graciously handed back half-a-crown, presumably to show he wasn't a complete capitalist, and much handshaking and consuming of cake, and of course the ubiquitous sherry, took place.

Moreover, mutual grievances and complaints could be aired in a fair and frank way, and many a farmer went away the happier for telling the squire, however haltingly, exactly what he thought of him. Of course, there were some overlords who had difficulty accepting this arrangement, and Lord Netherbourne, when accused of allowing his son to philander with a farmer's under-housemaid daughter, retaliated by demanding that all his tenants' sons should join the Yeomanry at Hollerton – hardly cricket! Thankfully, another few rounds of sherry put the matter in perspective, and the farmer used his shotgun to take a few of Lord Netherbourne's prime game birds instead of the revenge he may have originally planned.

Sadly, the gentry don't always figure too well in our survey of rural customs and traditions. Which brings me to the delicate subject of hunting.

I have to say, I suffer a crisis of conscience here, torn as I am between causes – that of wildlife management versus rural tradition, which also incorporates cottage industry. On the one hand, I agree that foxes are very attractive creatures, but I can well understand why Jill Archer might object when she can't give her B&B guests fresh free-range eggs for breakfast because a fox has laid waste in the hen house – extremely distressing, especially for townie guests who can be very squeamish in the face of feathers, fur, mud and … well, dung! Guests whose children are still coming to terms with milk from cows, not waxed supermarket cartons!

If only the huntsman and the farmer could be friends.

But if you happen to be visiting Ambridge on the first Saturday in November, I do recommend you try to see the South Borsetshire Hunt's Opening Meet outside the Bull – a wonderful but most traditional sight, and one that is fast disappearing, due as much to farmers prohibiting hunting across their valuable arable land as to the Anti-Blood Sports Lobby.

It is quite likely that the demise of the Hunt will allow poachers *carte blanche* to lay traps for everything that moves, and I dread a repeat of the time Hermes got caught in a snare in Leader's Wood – it was only George Barford's timely intervention that prevented a tragedy.

However, to continue our theme of significant seasonal scenarios, which brings me to 11th November, Martinmas. Combining, as it does, the peak pig-killing period with the final fermentation of cider brewing, Martinmas represents the best in Ambridge survival culture.

I think Joe Grundy's pithy, if vulgar, comment, 'Killin' time a-comin' up, Missus. Kill yer pig and bung your barrel!' sums up the importance of this tradition which dates back to the Middle Ages when every pig, except the breeders, was killed and salted.

People expected a lot from theirs pigs in those days and, along with the hams, bacons, sausages and pork pies, they managed to produce black pudding, saveloys, chitterlings, faggots and brawn. I'm glad to say I have never tasted any of these delicacies, not even for the sake of research but, revolting as they may sound and look, one must concede that they remain a wonderful example of good husbandry and natural recycling and, no doubt, when accompanied by Joe Grundy's apple sauce and cider, they would be almost palatable.

I did seek an audience with Jean-Paul on the subject of black pudding *et al.*, and though he had obviously decided to speak in monosyllabic patois, his feelings were quite clear. In fact, they are not repeatable here and would probably add little to Elizabeth David's more sanguine views, but it seems that he advises devotees to visit the Cafe Cochon, somewhere in the Loire Valley, to experience the *vrai chose* – anything else is *une bouffe*!

I shall conclude this dip into Ambridge rural traditions with two major annual events – the Ambridge Village Fete and the Flower and Produce Show – since, in some ways, they overlap and complement each other as symbols of village life.

Village fetes go back generations and probably evolved from the travelling fairs of the Middle Ages. These were great opportunities for communication, commerce and entertainment in an otherwise pretty dreary existence. Strolling players, musicians, acrobats, magicians and, of course, morris men, all contributed to the colourful motley of the fair. Stalls of fresh produce or silks and laces were set out, beasts were fattened for sale, and no doubt some poor wretch was chained in the stocks or a dancing bear was paraded to add a little *piquance* to the standard entertainment.

Yes, I'm sorry to say, that sort of thing, and worse, was very prevalent in those days and serves to remind us that people's sense of humour was very crude and limited. I don't think there's anything funny about being stuck in the stocks with people throwing disgusting objects at one, and I don't mind admitting that if such a misfortune ever befell me, I'd feel like throwing in the sponge!

How fortunate we are, then, to live in more enlightened times! Leaping on, therefore, to the 1950s, one is relieved to discover that a diet of wartime comedy radio shows, like *ITMA*, followed by the *nouvelle vague* of *The Goon Show*, had had a refining effect on the prevailing humour of the day, and people tended to laugh at absolutely ridiculous inanities rather than the cruel vulgarity of earlier times.

The fete, as it had now become, was always held in the grounds of the Manor, presided over by the Lawson-Hopes, with much bunting and tea served in the conservatory.

There was a cinema tent showing old films (much appreciated in those pre-video days, I should think) and penny pony rides and boat trips on the lake. You could even get lost in the maze for a halfpenny and, at the end of the afternoon, all the produce was auctioned off and the squire was officially thanked for allowing the fete this charming setting.

Could this be an ancient folk dance handed down from Molly the Witch? (Note the latter-day broomstick.)

It's all very reminiscent of the sort of lovely old British film made at Denham or Shepperton Studios that Robert and I indulge in on occasional Saturdays when hay fever demands an afternoon inside with the TV. They usually star Googie Withers and John McCallum, with Denis Price as the butler and Miles Malleson as the old retainer. (On reflection, I think I might have cast Phyllis Calvert and David Farrer as the Lawson-Hopes, Cecil Parker as the butler, and possibly A. E. Matthews or even Finlay Currie as the old retainer – I think they would have exactly complemented all that chintz and oak panelling.)

In recent years, the village green has become home to the fete, but it is not without its problems, like the year that Marjorie Antrobus went into over-drive because the grass was in such bad condition and she thought she might have to cancel. It was then that I, happy to assume Lady Lettie's mantle, as it were, offered her the use of our grounds at Ambridge Hall – with tea in the conservatory as an alternative extra.

Well, I can imagine Lady Lettie turning in her grave with embarrassment when my offer was declined, but only after I had told everyone to turn up at the Hall! This fickle trait in the village character has only surfaced since the decline of feudalism, I fear, and I am relieved that Lady Lettie is no longer with us to experience the hurt I felt on her behalf.

But back to the Big Day! It must have been tales of the year of the Victorian Cricket Match, ladies versus gentlemen, with costumes borrowed from BADS (Borchester Amateur Dramatic Society) – or was it FLOS (Felpersham Light Operatic Society) – that inspired me to suggest a fancy dress parade one year. Of course, I appeared as Elizabeth I, in a costume loosely based on her famous Armada portrait by George Gower. Unfortunately, it rained – heavily enough to turn my magnificent Elizabethan ruff into a doily, but *not* heavily enough to prevent Joe Grundy from taking photographs of people 'wearing' his parrot! *Did* he go as Long John Silver? It's possible, I suppose – I think I'd rather not remember.

I dread to think how a downpour might have affected the ladies' crinolines at the Victorian cricket match.

Typical events of the day include the raft race, when nearly everyone capsizes much to the huge enjoyment of the onlookers. Then there is the bonnie baby competition; the dog-most-like-its-owner competition for the Captain Memorial Trophy (Jack Woolley was touchingly besotted with this depressing animal, *not* that I'm suggesting for one moment that there is anything depressing about Mr Woolley – he is a very …*special* employer – but, one makes the usual allowances); the tug-a-truck team of women, led by Clarrie Grundy, which had spectacular success over the men one year; and wellie wanging – I'm not quite sure what this is, and I'm reluctant to enquire because it sounds like Grundy territory, but I believe it's quite diverting, if somewhat violent. Of course, the Edgeley Morris Dancers are inevitably present throughout along with the Hollerton Silver Band, maybe starring George Barford's solo trumpet – *if* he isn't in temperament mode.

And of course, the Year of the Litter was something of a miracle for me, carried, as I was from one key strategic point to another, smiling through the pain, advising and monitoring, and occasionally being sedated by Kathy Perks who looked happily harassed in her St John Ambulance outfit.

The WI are everywhere and it usually rains before the afternoon is over, but this is England – I'm glad to say – so everyone is expected to do their duty, defy the elements, and carry out the necessary rescue operation to wrecked trestle tables and the like, before retiring home, tired, but happy!

Visitors could be forgiven for assuming that the Flower and Produce Show is of a similar nature, but don't be fooled – for one thing, it takes place in the village hall in early autumn and, despite the sleepy turn of the season, the tension in the air is tangible.

Everyone who is anyone has a rural reputation at stake here. You will see dazzling displays of immaculate fruit and vegetables, burnished to a plump sheen; dahlias and chrysanthemums, picturesquely poised by Jill Archer, or insouciant wildflower arrangements, hastily improvised by Brenda Tucker; jams, pickles, cakes (the WI again), home-made wine and corn dollies – all arranged with precision and some taste, and all hoping to win the coveted Lawson-Hope Challenge Cup for the best entry in the show.

The most notorious rivalry is between Tom Forrest and Bert Fry – almost qualifying for the title of GVR – and I'm sorry to say that, fond as I am of both these genuine countrymen, neither of them is known for abiding by the Queensberry Rules. In other words, they'll stop at nothing to sabotage each other's patient handiwork. I shall refrain from quoting examples for fear of provoking the dreaded copy-cat syndrome but, take it from me, midnight marauding is nothing to those two, and the vengeance they can wreak is terrible indeed.

What usually happens is that Bert wins the prize for the most prepos-terous (though not to him) pumpkin, and Tom walks away with the prize for the mightiest marrow. Imagine his pique when *I* actually managed to win this one year (though with seeds donated by him).

More recently, Janet Fisher was the judge both at the Flower and Produce Show and at the fete – a nice gesture and I think she was pleased to be asked, but it was obvious that she has never actually grown anything since the broad-bean-on-blotting-paper experiment at school! Well, I don't think she realised it, but by giving Tom first prize for his potatoes, second for his onions, and Bert Fry third for both, she was virtually fanning the existing flame of rivalry into a full-blown GVR!

Tom's triumphalism was only barely containable, and if Freda Fry hadn't had the good sense to get Bert out of the way as soon as possible, well . . . I shrink from contemplating the ugly scene that would have ensued.

I have a sneaking suspicion that Janet may have been playing a polit-ical card, because she needed Tom's support in organising the special peal of bells to mark the opening of the Dan Archer Memorial Playground. There is a plaque on the church wall commemorating the peal of the Five Thousand and Forty Grandsire Doubles rung on 1st October 1896, very near the date of Dan's birth, and as Tom's grandfather was one of the original ringers, 'the knowledge', as it were, is likely to be in his genes.

Of course, I offered to handle the whole delicate business for Janet, but she changed the subject – rather too abruptly, I thought. I soon realised why when she awarded me second prize for my chrysanthemums and Usha Gupta

Little has changed in the Bull over the decades – try eavesdropping here and you will soon pick up on current GVRs.

first for her rudbeckias, thus proving how perceptive I had been about Janet and flowers. After all, as anyone who has wrestled with the life-cycle of the average chrysanthemum knows, rudbeckias are hardly rhodochitons, are they?

Richard and Auntie Satya were naturally very supportive of Usha's efforts, not that I think Richard would know rudbeckias from rhubarb. But Tom was positively effusive – well, for him, that is – and I wouldn't be the least bit surprised if he had been keeping a friendly eye on Usha's cloches from time to time. Not that I begrudge Usha a little expert advice, even if she should be disqualified for taking it, especially when she walks off with first prize!

After all, anything which encourages her to stay on at Blossom Hill Cottage with Richard, must, of itself, be of benefit to the social development of life in Ambridge. Actually, I have great hopes of Auntie Satya advising her to tidy up her front garden, instead of embarking on such supposedly ambitious projects as raising rudbeckias! If only to give the humble chrysanthemum growers a sporting chance in next year's competition!

I do recommend you try to coincide your visit to Ambridge with the Flower and Produce Show – in a way it represents, in microcosm, everything about Ambridge society that you'll ever need to know!

A magnet to the stars at any Ambridge event – even when pilloried.

Poet & Peasant

An overview of the artistic, creative side of Ambridge

It is no exaggeration to say that England is a nation of thespians and *not*, as Napoleon would have had it, a 'nation of shop-keepers' which was his second biggest mistake, after the Siege of Moscow, and probably explains why we won the Napoleonic Wars and he ended up in exile!

But it remains a fascinating paradox that the English, so celebrated for their reserve and stiff upper-lip, can become raving extroverts given half a chance. Not that one would presume to exclude the Irish, Welsh or Scots from possessing a talent for exhibitionism, as you will know if you've ever spent Hogmanay in Glasgow!

It does mean, though, that in the meanest village, hamlet or cul-de-sac the length and breadth of 'this sceptr'd isle', there lurks an amateur dramatic society! I'm sorry, but there it is – everyone is a wannabe actor, and when produc-tion week finally arrives, usually after months of rehearsal, the normally phlegmatic Englishman, given doublet and hose, fake beard and a couple of sticks of greasepaint to play with, is perfectly capable of throwing a temperament of alarming proportions.

In Ambridge, this phenomenon is manifested by total disinterest, nay, apathy, right up until the eleventh hour when there is a rush of frenzied activity and a performance, followed by the near nervous breakdown of the producer

Dame Edna was overwhelmed by this picture.

screaming 'Never again!' and a self-congratulatory party where everyone is known as 'Dahling!' for the rest of the evening.

But in heritage terms, Ambridge's artistic past is somewhat shadowy (though not quite to the extent of being designated a twilight zone) due to the fortunate accident of the Bard living just up the road in Stratford-upon-Avon. Indeed, he would undoubtedly have passed through Ambridge on his way to London for important first nights of *Othello*, *Hamlet* and *The Dream*, and would often stop for a pint of Shires, notebook in hand, listening in on the locals chattering away and hoping to get some useful authentic dialogue out of the encounter. So, next time you see a production of *The Merchant of Venice*, look out for 'eanlings', meaning new dropped lambs, or, in *Love's Labour's Lost* ('Look how he claws him') 'claw', meaning to flatter. You will hear hedgehogs referred to as 'urchins' in *Titus Andronicus*, and a game of skittles called 'loggatts' in *Hamlet*.

These are just a few of the local words and expressions – still to be heard on the lips of Joe Grundy and Tom Forrest (though *not* Bert Fry, who despises artistic plagiarism, he says!) – that Shakespeare would have scribbled down to weave into a piece of iambic pentameter later on. By employing the age-old creative principles of 'writing about what you know' and 'giving the people what they want', he pretty well guaranteed a good following in Borsetshire, though I doubt that his more sophisticated fans at court would have had a clue what he was talking about.

After Shakespeare's time, there seemed to be a literary lull in and around Ambridge – or so it would seem from the dearth of documentation available in Borchester Reference Library.

However, I have to report that my research did reveal the unfortunate saga of one Josiah Goodall, an eighteenth-century local poet and libertine from Darrington (which explains much!) who was supposed to have married an Ambridge girl, Tabitha Thorncroft. I had been prepared to evaluate my findings in a quite positive light until I read Jennifer Aldridge's outrageous article in the *Borchester Echo* which glamourised his appalling behaviour to rock-star status and had Mr Woolley wanting to name a suite at Grey Gables after him!

According to Jennifer Aldridge – not known for the thoroughness of her research, I might add – he was an agricultural radical who spent more time womanising than writing poetry and was finally deported to America for sheep stealing and much besides. All very interesting, though I am not fooled for one moment by Jennifer Aldridge's views, aimed as they are, as a deliberate slur on my own research into that gentleman's biography.

My own theory is that he was out carousing with sundry wenches one night and deliberately walked into the village pond, probably for a wager.

Here, he slipped on the slimy bottom and drowned in a drunken stupor while his companions rolled about with helpless laughter on the bank, shouting, 'Good riddance to bad rubbish!'

I'm quite convinced that all this nonsense about deportation was to create a local folk hero at a time when everyone was feeling very down-trodden and the notion of 'local boy makes good and finds a new life in the colonies' was most appealing. In fact, it is chronicled that there was a sharp nation-wide rise in the incidence of sheep stealing and other appropriate crimes around this time, obviously in the hope of getting on the deportation bandwagon.

As for the quality of his work – well, we have Al and Mary-Jo Clancy, the visiting Americans, to thank for dredging up a poem which even Hayley would have been ashamed of and which Bert would have shredded for compost. I am not prepared to quote it here since I still suffer the memory of Al Clancy's quivering rendition at breakfast one morning. In fact, so moved was he by Goodall's 'clarion call to his fellow radicals', as he fulsomely described it, that I was tempted to wonder if there may have been truth in the deportation story after all, and that the Clancys could have been descended from Goodall's American philanderings without actually realising it! I felt it wiser not to share this alarming thought with them for fear of encouraging them to stay longer, and I was already all out of maple syrup and zest of lime.

Actually, they showed no serious signs of Goodall genes, apart from a total lack of taste in their farewell surprise gift – I have a feeling that a pink, plastic, padded loo seat would have sent Josiah into poetic paroxysms of delight!

Josiah Goodall thinking about writing a poem.

I decided the moment had come to access Ambridge's current man of letters, Bert Fry, who has already proved himself to be an ingenious source of information on . . . well, pretty well anything you care to name, really.

I should explain that, for me, Bert combines all the best traditions of the countryside with a creative, artistic instinct. His mastery of the rhyming couplet first reached a wider audience than his cronies in the Bull when Elizabeth Pargetter invited him to write a weekly column of country sayings in the *Borchester Echo*. So successful was his prolific pen that someone (and I think it may have been Elizabeth, desperately trying to divert the over-whelming flood of verse threatening to swamp her in-tray) alerted the local TV company – with disastrous results!

I am sorry to say that becoming an overnight star went straight to Bert's head. He arrived at the studios sporting a rather poetic pink shirt. All the more shocking because Bert has never been known to wear a shirt, except on Sundays in church and then always of a startlingly starched white!

Imagine his chagrin when the producer insisted that he wore 'an arty-farty smock, like one of them country bumpkins in *A Midsummer Night's Dream*. I told 'im, "I ain't no rude mechanical!" But he wouldn't 'ave it!'

It didn't stop there, however. When Phil Archer wanted to give Willow Cottage to David and Ruth, Bert refused to vacate because it would ruin his image – apparently, his fans had seen a photo of him taken outside Willow Cottage and his duty was to keep faith with them.

The final straw came when the poster he came up with for my production of *The Importance of Being Earnest* read, 'Featuring TV personality, Bert Fry'!

I was shocked to think that Bert's artistic integrity could be so easily seduced by cheap media hype. But I decided to cling to my conviction that, as a man, first and foremost of the soil, he could never be completely beguiled by transitory eminence.

So when I came across him in the churchyard at St Stephen's, stuffing handfuls of comfrey and deadly nightshade into black plastic bags, I felt quite justified in quoting the Bard's *Titus Andronicus* at him: 'He lives in fame that died in virtue's cause.'

I had hoped to strike some sort of chord in his poetic soul. 'Cor, I hate that play,' was his reply. 'It ain't nothin' but bits of bodies gettin' chopped off!' Once again, Bert had surprised me by his intimate acquaintance with the less popular works of Shakespeare, and others.

I felt myself on the horns of a dilemma: should I interrogate Bert further as to the source of his privileged information? Could he, unknown to Freda, be embroiled in a secret Open University course on 'Murder and mayhem v. lawr'n order in Elizabethan drama'? If so, perhaps it was kinder – and safer! –

not to encourage his enthusiastic, if pointless, discourse on the fruits of his learning, and merely allow him to continue his worthy, if pointless, efforts to tidy up an overgrown corner of the churchyard.

As if reading my thoughts, he said he'd had enough of tidying up for one week, 'what with the moles an' all,' and was pulling up comfrey to make a super liquid feed for his potatoes and onions – 'so bloomin' Tom Forrest can kiss goodbye to first prize at the Flower and Produce Show this year!'

When I asked what he intended doing with the deadly nightshade, he replied, 'Ah, well! I ain't decided – yet – I'm still workin' on it. But the Elizabethans would 'a known what to do with it, that's fer sure!' and he looked rather meaningful, I thought. So I deemed it the moment for flattery and complimented him on his Bardic sagacity, beside which even mine seemed thin and nerveless.

'Oh, I come down from Shakespeare – he's in me blood, like. But afore him, I come down from Freya, the Norse goddess of romantic love. That's where Fry comes from, see?'

Suddenly, it all made sense – Bert's poetic soul was rooted in Viking mythology, along with Wagner and Co.!

I left him sitting on a gravestone, crushing deadly nightshade into a pot of Bridge Farm yoghourt — blackcurrant flavour, for camouflage — muttering something unintelligible which could have been:

> *I will arise*
> *And win that prize.*
> *With this deadly pot*
> *I'll win the lot.*

But I prefer to think he was merely trying out wicked witch dialogue for the next panto.

Speaking of which, I consider this to be an optimum moment to discuss my own personal involvement in pantomime and, indeed, the many other presentations I have facilitated over the decade.

I must admit they do all tend to become a sort of blur in the memory, with present clarity depending on the varying degrees of success or distress I sustained during production. But I think I can honestly say that I have seriously striven to carry on the dramatic tradition handed down by the Bard, our 'Writer in Residence', as it were – still with

One of my great strengths is my ability to rally the locals together for cultural activities of all kinds.

us in spirit. In fact, I think he would feel gratified to learn that I have considered devising my own Shakespearean one-woman show entitled 'Shakespeare's woman – heroine or harridan?' and comprising all the great female speeches including Lady Macbeth's mad scene which, as Fabian Windrush, resident leading man of the Sunningdale players once said, could have been written for me!

But I have a sneaking feeling that the idea wouldn't go down too well with Jill Archer who, since succumbing to the cloying flattery of Laurence Lovell by allowing herself to be cast as the Wicked Stepmother in *Cinderella*, believes she has cornered the market in villainesses and is doubtless now persuading Larry to do Daphne du Maurier's *Rebecca* just so that she can play Mrs Danvers to his Max de Winter.

Having been encouraged by the oozing pleasantries of LL, she may even, see herself as Ambridge's answer to Dame Peggy Ashcroft. I, on the other hand, prefer to see myself as Ambridge's answer to Dame Sibyl Thorndike, which is why I'm

Felpersham Cathedral – the perfect venue for my proposed production of St Joan.

hoping that Bishop Cyril will let me mount a production of *St Joan* (starring and directed by myself) in Felpersham Cathedral, to celebrate the Millennium. I don't expect a refusal – I know how well he remembers the year that Ambridge formed part of the massed choirs singing Handel's *Messiah*. Nor shall I ever forget the look on his face as I rescued the melodically challenged sopranos in the second reprise of the 'Hallelujah Chorus' – and I think I can safely say that Bishop Cyril is not a man who would forget a favour, or decline to honour it. And I'm sure he will want to address my need to confront my disappointing experience in Rouen all those years ago by acting out the story of my girlhood heroine, in public, in Felpersham Cathedral.

Of course, my earliest memory of drama in Ambridge was a Christmas morality play in which everyone was supposed to speak with authentic mediaeval accents. It was intended to replace the pantomime, but was almost a pantomime itself, at least in terms of casting (see *right* for final result).

COL. DANBY – EVERYMAN

WALTER GABRIEL – LUST

MARJORIE ANTROBUS – KNOWLEDGE

MARTHA WOODFORD – DISCRETION

JACK WOOLLEY – WORLDLY GOODS

JOE GRUNDY – DEATH

This is reputedly when Joe first became aware of his unnatural obsession with death, though he was denied the chance to explore this during performance because the production was called off. I can't remember why – probably because the mediaeval accents got out of hand. In the end, Tom Forrest came to the rescue with *all* the verses of 'The Village Pump' and other traditional ballads, and the event sank without much trace.

However, it did leave Joe Grundy with his unfortunate obsession, which next manifested itself during rehearsals for my Christmas production of *Pot Pourri* when Joe's interminable rendition of 'Christmas Day in the Workhouse' ran a close second to his 'Hob Hound' ode in the morbidly depressed stakes.

I am ashamed to say that I had put myself in a situation which I regret to this day – a clash between my artistic integrity and my loyalty to a conservationist cause – and all because, in a misguided moment, I had foolishly agreed to allow Joe to perform the above poem in return for his active presence at the David Archer v. the Ancient Hedgerow confrontation (cross-refer to 'Feudin', Fussin' & A'Fighting'). Needless to say, Joe wouldn't permit editing a single gloomy verse – there were about sixty! – and I had to drop Phil Archer's singalong (fun for the masses) and Christine Barford's charming rendition of Thomas Hardy's 'The Oxen' (thoughtful and seasonal) from the programme.

Mutiny was only narrowly avoided by my inspired introduction of a double act between Nelson and myself as Noel and Gertie, compering the show in seasonal style and singing a character-duet version of 'Little Drummer Boy'. I know Nelson had been looking forward to working with me on this (our voices blend so well, and we both have such a feeling for style) but what should have been an upbeat novelty number was hi-jacked by Marjorie Antrobus's pettifogging behaviour, already discussed and really not worthy of further reference (cross-refer to 'Ghosties and Ghoulies').

The evening came to an abrupt end, amidst much raucous audience participation. Indeed, such were the high spirits of the occasion that, at the party at the Hall afterwards, everyone thought Joe's recitation had been hysterically funny – and for one ghastly moment, I feared he might betray my 'arrangement' with him, out of pique. But he merely shrugged and said, ''Course it were funny – it were meant to be! That's known as satire, that is. Ain't you ever watched *Monty Python*?'

Well, as you can imagine, this unexpected piece of erudition silenced the room as everyone covered their confusion by passing round the extra sandwiches – so kindly, but unnecessarily, provided by Simon and Shula to eke out my meagre offerings (though I'm sure they were kindly meant, by Shula, anyway!). In fact, despite everything, that evening raised a handsome donation to Dan Archer's Playground Fund, proving that it is possible to produce a silk purse from a pig's ear by applying a little TLC – Talent, Leadership and Confidence!

But I remain intrigued by Joe Grundy's momentary lapse into literary mode. I can only think that in his early youth, he attended the Ambridge Reading Room where, for a shilling a quarter, local labourers and tradesmen could spend evenings reading books and newspapers, thus generally improving the gaps in their scant education. Who knows, but that the young Joe may have chosen as a subject for his compulsory monthly essay, the title 'The satirical style of Dryden and Pope – compare and contrast'.

If only one could get close enough to Joe to draw his literary light from under its bushel! But the closest I have ever got to Joe was playing the back legs to his front legs of Daisy the Cow, in my controversial Europanto, *Sleeping Beauty*, and I'm afraid it is not an experience I would wish to repeat, even for the sake of plumbing Joe's untapped creative depths.

I shall never forget the hours of insomnia *Sleeping Beauty* caused me. In a way, it was my own fault for putting so much faith in the available talent, which seemed to diminish in availability (and talent!) at the mere mention of rehearsals! But I felt the time was ripe for artistic challenge, for stretching the boundaries – for improvisation in other words! Well, you'd have thought they didn't know what I was talking about, which was pretty depressing for someone with my communication skills.

I hoped to achieve a melt-down situation by giving them a brief lecture on 'The history of early Italian *Commedia dell Arte*' where the actors improvised, wearing masks, and the comic scenes were left to the actor's own invention. This style was in turn rooted in the bawdy comedies of ancient Rome and then, much later, took on French influence before finally coming to England in the form we know as pantomime.

As you might expect, Eddie Grundy said he didn't mind having a go at a bawdy improvisation! In fact, we did play a few trust games – standing in a circle and catching the blindfolded person in the centre who allows him/herself to be pushed pivotally from side to side of the circle. But this ended in tears because Eddie insisted on cuddling Clarrie when she landed in his arms, and Joe kept dropping anyone who landed in his! Susan Carter nearly walked out in a huff, saying she wouldn't trust Eddie Grundy with her eyes *open*, never mind blindfolded, which resulted in a heated exchange between her and Clarrie.

In desperation, I suggested we should explore the various scenarios of how the Prince should waken Sleeping Beauty, in a Euro-context, that is – by

Eddie has never forgotten his trip to Birmingham to see Britt Ekland in pantomime – and neither has Britt.

mobile phone? Or perhaps pager? Or maybe infiltrate her web-site? But I could see nothing was going to gel from the way they all started putting their coats on and heading for the door, so I gave in and wrote the script myself.

As it turned out, the whole thing was postponed until the following March due to lack of interest, but people did rally at last, and I was very pleased with the final performance.

However, I didn't even *contemplate* the possibility of improvisation in my production of *Aladdin*, and took the precaution of writing the script *well* in advance. The fact that it was about seven years in advance was neither here nor there – it had achieved critical acclaim, in Sunningdale in 1984, despite

Fabian Windrush's very inebriated Widow Twanky and Doreen Puretoy's black fishnets, and I was quite shocked by the village hall Committee's negative attitude; *of course* I would have updated references to the miner's strike.

Ironically, it was this very clash of artistic interests which was instrumental in nominating 1991 as 'The Year of the Two Aladdins'. Bert Fry had had the audacity to write a rival script (so much for loyalty!) which for some obscure reason, was accepted as the *official* production for performance at the village hall.

This left me no option but to unflinchingly accept the challenge and throw down the gauntlet by producing my own version of *Aladdin* in the conservatory at Ambridge Hall, starring Debbie Aldridge as Aladdin, Joe Grundy as Abanazer and Eddie Grundy as Wishee Washee.

I'm sure that, to this day, Bert remains ignorant of the facts, but I was under no illusion about what was going on, though I chose, as always, to keep my counsel. But from the breathlessly garbled manner in which Eddie delivered his lines in performance – lines which I would have been incapable of writing – it was quite clear that Eddie was spreading himself rather too thinly between my conservatory and the village hall. I was surprised that Clarrie had stooped so low as to collude with him in this deception, but how else could he have appeared as Wishee Washee in both productions, at the *same* time, if she hadn't driven him back and forth and Velcroed him in and out of his respective costumes?

I seemed to go into temporary retreat after that painful episode and sought consolation in redesigning my garden, but not before removing the Velcro from all clothing apertures – the flaps of my gardening over-shoes, the inner wind-proof cuffs of Robert's squall jacket and the tops of my waders (kept specifically for village pond-dredging expeditions) – and applying hooks and eyes instead. That noisome ripping sound had, in my hyper-sensitive state, become synonymous with Eddie in quick-change mode, and I lived under permanent threat of a migraine for quite some time afterwards.

I even insisted on hooks and eyes when I made the children's costumes for *A Village at War* – my video of the Battle of Hassett Bridge, recreated by Richard Locke and his chums in the Sealed Knot group. I don't think

Richard Locke particularly upstanding in his regalia for the re-enactment of the Battle of Hassett Bridge.

Susan Carter will ever forgive me for what those hooks and eyes did to her false nails, but as I pointed out to her, were false nails a wise move in the circumstances? And it was essential for the children to look authentically seventeenth century in close-up. She said, in that case, she expected to see *lots* of close-ups of her Emma!

Yes, I'm afraid we are never far away from pushy theatrical mothers, even in Ambridge, but I blame myself for even mentioning that Emma had some talent – I mean, we're not talking Shirley Temple or Bonnie Langford. Susan has certainly come a long way in her quest for status and respectability, and no-one can deny she has had much to contend with – after all, the combination of an unfair prison sentence, a known felon for a brother and working for Simon Pemberton might have overwhelmed lesser mortals. The fact remains that even such character-building experiences could never prepare her for the role of mother to a child star, let alone that of theatrical chaperone – many have been called, but few have been chosen, *and* survived!

However, I cannot leave the pantomimic theme without a passing reference to what was to have been *my* production of *Cinderella*, and which was monstrously purloined from my jurisdiction by Laurence Lovell.

I should explain that Laurence Lovell is to Ambridge what Doreen Purefoy is to Sunningdale, fishnets notwithstanding. Think *parvenu*, think charlatan, think *poseur*, think social-climbing rank amateur and you get the picture! Robert suggested that Laurence Lovell probably *is* Doreen Purefoy – in drag! Rather OTT for Robert, but I take his point.

The tragedy of Cinderella could so easily have been averted if Bert and Hayley had not colluded over the script and allowed LL (as I shall now refer to him) to usurp my customary role of author, executive producer and performer – though only in parts that do justice to my ability.

As it was, Robert and I returned from holiday in Kansas, too late to prevent a coup, to find that LL had simply moved in and deftly assumed power, though not without frequent thrusts and parries from me. I probably made myself unpopular with the rest of the cast – something which never happens when I hold the reins – but I'm afraid I refused to stand by and watch his sloppy direction, his ingratiating acceptance of mediocrity and, most of all, his fawning over Jill Archer as the Wicked Stepmother, a part that could have been written for me and which I had set my heart on ever since Doreen Purefoy (DP from now on) had wrested it from me in Sunningdale.

It was when Julia Pargetter entered stage-left as choreographer that I knew the writing was on the dressing-room wall, so to speak – this was DP revisited! It was insulting enough to have been cast as the Good Fairy, but to be denied the chance to enrich my trite little scenes by dint of employing the three Is (Invention, Imagination and Intuition) was really too much! There was a hideous scene at rehearsals in which LL became quite hysterical, refusing to countenance any opinion but his own – fairly typical of a former West End understudy who had never actually gone on in *The Desert Song*!

It was quite impossible for me to give my best work in such conditions, so I withdrew from the production, leaving LL and JA to act out their secret assignations over coffee in Underwoods, and the rest of the cast in despair. I did find a window in my schedule to take Jill aside for a little basic psychotherapy – just the common-sense approach, reminding her of *ars longa, vita brevis*, and should she really cast aside the hempen smock and halting tongue of Phil Archer for the flowery fantasies and silken insouciance of LL?

I think I timed this move with my usual flair because her presenting symptoms were of a woman about to embark on something she would later be unable to contain, judging by the shifty way she kept averting her face during our conversation. But I'm glad to say that my words struck home and, post-panto, she seems to have settled down to being a grandmother for the third time and running her B&B, and is altogether a much better person.

Which brings me back to the first night of *Cinderella*, arriving, as it did, minus myself as the Good Fairy, though not for long. Ever the trouper, I simply couldn't let my audience down – I actually made my entrance from the back of the auditorium, thus completely upstaging LL who was, by now, in the middle of a pitiful attempt to double as both Baron Hardup *and* the Good Fairy.

It was a triumphant *coup de théatre* which left LL speechless in the face of wild applause at my bravura! We declared a tacit truce at the party afterwards, but I remain vigilant *à propos* LL, and have already had to warn Caroline that he is, *au fond*, a *rouet manqué* as well as an *artiste manqué*!

In fact, I believe he has, at last, duped some innocent on the committee of FLOS or BADS (I forget which) into letting him loose on *The Desert Song* – no doubt produced by and starring himself, as the Red Shadow! Will he be 'hoist with his own petard', one wonders? I certainly don't intend to find out – triumphalism has never appealed to me!

I must say, the final denouement of the *Cinderella* saga, hinging, as it did, on my inventive *volte-face* from disadvantaged outsider to acclaimed team-leader, struck me as reminiscent of a similar experience I had with Dame Edna Everage. Little did she know that our encounter in the theatre that evening was to inspire my dismissal of LL to the rank of has-been years later, and I have contemplated dropping her a fax or an E-mail on the subject, since I know any little incidents demonstrating *la condition humaine* are meat and drink to her – in a caring way, of course. But unfortunately, web-sites and fax numbers were not on the agenda that evening.

It was during the second half of the show that she spotted me in the second row of the stalls – Robert had bought the most expensive seats in the house and then, pleading shyness, insisted on trying to conceal himself between the floor and the opera glasses machine! Unsuccessfully, I might add!

Dame Edna was very interested in my views on interior design but, though we had a full and frank discussion, it became obvious that she was trying to entertain the audience by making cheap jibes at my expense. However, I'm delighted to say I held my own throughout, and the audience had so warmed to me that, by the time I joined her on stage as part of her chat show, it was very much a case of 'Collapse of Stout Party' for poor Dame Edna. Her final downfall came during 'The Gladdi Song' when I found myself leading the audience in a rousing chorus which completely drowned her rather cracked and tuneless falsetto.

Robert was very quiet on the way home – too moved to speak I suspect – but I did get him to agree that, without question, I had upstaged a megastar!

Robert was overwhelmed by this one.

Ambridge was singularly unimpressed by my reportage of the event, until, that is, the *Cinderella* episode eight years later, when I think there was probably a lot of humble pie being eaten behind closed doors!

Of course, Ambridge does attract some celebrated professional performers – Lower Loxley provides a gracious setting and many visitors to Grey Gables plan their stay to coincide with some of the distinguished musical events on offer (leaflets available at Reception on request).

Thus it was that a visiting opera company's production of Mozart's *Don Giovanni* swam into our ken. I am happy to say that I was able to avert a near disaster by stepping, fully-costumed, into the breach at rehearsals when Angie, the soprano, got lost! Fortunately, as a Mozart devotee, I knew the entire score by heart, as I told the producer when he almost begged me to take over in performance. Angie eventually turned up, saying that though she was now found her voice remained lost, and her top Cs could be a thing of the past!

The producer, rather misguidedly, decided to engage a relief soprano who, as I predicted, was … well, a mistake! She arrived late (only seconds before curtain-up) and very out of breath. Seeing me standing in the wings, in costume and practising my arpeggios, she was even more relieved to think that I was going to get her out of a nasty situation by going on in her place.

But the producer's word is law in a case like this, so I deemed it politic to retire gracefully to the back of the auditorium and take a few notes on what turned into a rather inferior performance, sadly. But I think the producer was grateful for my input – he was particularly impressed by my authentic eighteenth-century peasant costume, with shawl, and he promised to communicate my notes on her wayward top Cs to the unfortunate relief soprano.

In retrospect, I think it was just as well that *Don Giovanni* eluded me on that occasion – even a seasoned artist like myself can suffer from stage fright when performing in a less familiar medium. I think I have the humility to recognise that my true *métier* is as an exponent of the spoken rather than the

My costume was inspired by this illustration, though on reflection I banned the bonnet.

sung word, which is why I have refrained from joining FLOS (Felpersham Light Operatic Society). As you might expect, Jack and Peggy Woolley speak very highly of FLOS's recent productions of *Annie Get Your Gun* and *Flora Dora*, and have organised favourable discounts for visitors to Grey Gables. Those visitors who qualify are welcome to join the Over 60's twice-yearly coach party to FLOS's current contribution to the Franz Lehár canon – I believe that a trip to *The Land of Smiles* may even be in the pipeline (details available at Reception on request).

But, musically speaking, Ambridge had a surprisingly rich heritage long before my advent on the cultural scene, as I discovered from St Stephen's parish records. Apparently, for the Flower Festival in September 1981, a concert of mediaeval music was held to celebrate the church's dedication 700 years ago. The programme included music by Frescobaldi, various *chansons* of the twelfth and thirteenth centuries and even 'O Roma Nobilis' – an even earlier song of the Goliards – all played on the original instruments, namely, wide-bore recorder, psaltery, fifteenth-century spinet and krumhorn. The church warden of the day, whose signature is illegible I'm afraid, wrote:

'All the music was about seven-hundred-years old, written around the time that St Stephen's was dedicated and the musicians played their instruments, which were also very old, very nicely. It was very surprising to see so many people there as I, personally, didn't agree with having such outlandish music in the church and would have preferred a nice selection from Hymns Ancient and Modern, which everyone could join in with, and maybe 'Amazing Grace' on guitar for the younger folk (with permission from Philip Archer). But it all went down very well, and some people said we should have more of that sort of thing. Afterwards, everyone retired to the vicarage for a substantial finger buffet, courtesy of the bishop, and a very welcome glass of elderberry wine – 1975 vintage, kindly donated by Martha Woodford.'

Kenton Archer giving voice.

I'm not sure who was responsible for organising such a distinguished programme, nor from where such specialised players were procured, but clearly there existed in Ambridge an unexpected taste for the more exclusive types of music. What, if anything, has been done since to satisfy that demand? Nothing, in a word, so I approached Phil Archer (the only reliably musical person in Ambridge in my experience, despite occasional inconsistencies) to discuss how to fill this gaping void in Ambridge's cultural activities.

I can only assume he felt somehow threatened by my suggestion of organising a series of concerts featuring the works of Alban Berg, Stockhausen and Webern, for example, as an encouragement to the covert lovers of more specialised music genres to 'come out', as it were.

His response was sullen, to say the least: 'Well, I don't think anyone would come, Lynda, and it isn't really my cup of tea. We got an audience for the mediaeval music concert because it was part of the celebrations, but there were complaints about the krumhorns putting people's teeth on edge – in fact, I believe Walter Gabriel actually took his teeth out! I know they were found later by Marjorie Antrobus when she was collecting the hymn books.'

I have noticed, more than once, that Phil Archer has a tendency to be facetious when under fire. So I made it clear that I had come to him for facts, and that his bending of the truth for a cheap laugh was hardly worthy of a magistrate and church organist – or a disciple of Delia Smith! Moreover, it might behove him to redefine his interpretation of the word 'Green', since it certainly didn't coincide with mine!

And it was on this – yes, disappointed note! – that I concluded our debate on the musical future of Ambridge – but only for the time being, because I am delighted to say that, as part of my latest artistic thrust, I am devising two MAPs (Major Artistic Projects) with broad appeal to both local resident and visitor alike and designed to invigorate community spirit.

My first MAP, in musical vein, reflects my revival of traditional Ambridge concerts, before it is lost to a new generation. So, although I have not as yet declared my intentions to the parish council, I see my action plan as thus:

I envisage a series of seasonal heritage concerts, held throughout the year, very catholic in taste, but covering the needs of the 'silent élite', as I like to think of them, and with a local, even folklorique flavour. Each concert will be held in a different village venue, thus enticing the visitor to Ambridge with the opportunity to explore a variety of ambiances and modes of hospitality. All will richly reflect the cultural heritage of Ambridge.

Here is a draft *soupçon* of the kind of delights on offer:

Lost Lays of Lakey Hill: A cycle of troubadour *chansons*, loosely based on Tennyson's 'The Lady of Shalott' and Malory's 'Morte d'Arthur', rewritten in rhyming couplets or in free verse form (depending on mood) by Bert Fry, translated into mediaeval French, sung by Lynda Snell and set to music by Phil Archer (I'm expecting to get Phil's musical co-operation on this, simply by appealing to his vanity). To be performed in St Stephen's Church.

Bridge Farm Ballads: Written in pantomimic style by Hayley Jordan and performed on synthesiser by John Archer in the farm shop. Ticket price will include interval refreshments consisting of an organic picnic basket which will be consumed on the grass verge surrounding the carrot field, weather permitting. Please bring ground sheets but not insect repellent (eco-friendly organic version available).

Nightingale Nights: Victorian parlour songs in the conservatory at Ambridge Hall with the Ambridge Singers (yet to be appointed) accompanied by Marjorie Antrobus on the spinet.

The Village Pump – Your 101 Best Folk Tunes: A singalong, performed and led by Tom Forrest in the village hall.

Grange Grunge Night: A group activity (yet to be defined) in the cellars at Grange Farm, led by Kate Aldridge, Roy Tucker *et al*.

Melodramatic Monologues: A dinner recital by Joe Grundy in the Hassett Room, with boy-soprano highlights from Edward Grundy Jnr. Victorian menu to include beef Wellington, kedgeree and lots of things in aspic and moulds.

Hogmanay Hoe-Down: For New Year's Eve at the Bull, Eddie Grundy's country-and-western all-night extravaganza with ribs, cornbread in a basket and possibly Jolene Rogers. The programme could well include 'Like a Phoenix from the Flames'!

I am confident that it is possible to co-ordinate local musical talent in a programme of original and stimulating material, while exploiting some of our more attractive venues: Sid and Kathy will accept even an invasion of Grundys to increase trade at the Bull, and I know that Caroline would approve of such creative thinking. I would need to organise 'Operation Cellar Blitz' at Grange Farm – I wouldn't dream of asking Clarrie to descend the steps into what unknown horrors!

I think the conservatory recital would have to take place in winter in order to avoid savage attacks from white fly and red spider mite – they can be aggressively territorial during the summer months and, according to Robert who refuses to go anywhere near the conservatory in summer, they don't stop at sucking *blood* when they've run out of *sap!* 'Why do you think they're called *red* spider mite, Lyndy?'

Eddie Grundy – ever the phoenix.

With my second MAP, I have already gone public – yes! my idea for an al fresco production of *A Midsummer Night's Dream* came as a direct result of Robert not getting the job in Grimsby, a sort of blessing in disguise.

I think it was at the interview lunch, when I put the managing director's wife right about her choice of wine, that I sensed a problem. And though I continued to sparkle for Robert, as always – and the MD certainly appreciated my lightness of touch – I still feel (and Robert agrees with me) that it was the unmistakable resonance of Doreen Purefoy in the atmosphere that had a terminal effect on the proceedings.

So I shan't be strolling in People's Park, or exploring the wildlife of the Lincolnshire Wolds, or attending meetings of the Humberside International Women's Club (I had already been invited to join, my reputation for verve and creativity having somehow gone ahead of me) though I have granted them, as a consolation prize, the opportunity to make me an Honorary Member.

Rather sad in one way, and yet wonderfully focussing in another! Now that the future isn't looking grim, and Robert has accepted a more flexible work pattern, I can hurl myself wholeheartedly into rejuvenating the flagging thespian energies of Ambridge, and who would have thought it was that chance remark of Bert Fry's that was to be my inspiration …

. . . 'An arty-farty smock, like one of them country bumpkins in *A Midsummer Night's Dream*. I told 'im, "I ain't no rude mechanical!" But 'e wouldn't 'ave it!' I remember resisting the temptation not to react to this statement, but it must have imprinted somewhere in my subconscious, suddenly

Janet's churches and the Bull offer venues for events at each end of the cultural scale.

to erupt at the significant moment – a moment which defined for me the 'rightness' of not going to Grimsby! It was all so obvious – Robert and I were destined to stay in Ambridge, to enable the Bardic heritage to be represented by the descendants of those very 'rude mechanicals' who first inspired him to write the play! Thus it was, that *Murder in the Red Barn* gave way to *The Dream* in the dramatic scheme of things.

From the first, I didn't expect it to be easy – after all, I'm hardly likely to forget the level of commitment, efficiency and loyalty, let alone talent, that I can expect from a typical Ambridge cast! If only! But, as I reminded Sean when discussing *The Dream* stage settings, I cling fast to the words of Terence: 'Fortune favours the Brave.'

I have a feeling he assumed I was quoting Terence Rattigan rather than the great Roman poet, but at least he caught my drift – unlike Joe Grundy who arrived in my garden one morning and treated me to a truly grotesque delivery of a speech of Theseus's. It was this disturbing experience that inspired me to hold verse-speaking workshops on iambic pentameter, the rhythmic form of Shakespeare's writing.

I really should have recalled that one courts disaster when introducing any kind of theatrical workshop to the players of Ambridge (see the trust-game travesty discussed above). And I admit I hadn't thought my strategy through with my usual zeal – 'The readiness is all,' as the Bard knew only too well! But when Tom Forrest virtually accused me of Political Incorrectness, and insisted on delivering the Agincourt speech from *Henry V* (with great feeling) to prove that he, at least, was no 'rude mechanical', I could see I might be heading for a no-win situation.

Bert Fry, ever the poet, had already offered to rewrite *The Dream* in 'more up-to-date language that everyone can understand, Missus'! But I felt I had to persevere with exercises in metre and meaning, if only to appease the Bard who must, by now, have spun off into a black hole!

There were several unspeakable moments, like when Bert and Joe had the audacity to abuse the purity of iambic pentameter by making it a vehicle for exchanging petty insults and jealousies – Bert should really know better in view of his self-proclaimed Bardic blood. Then Jack Woolley, who should have had such potential as Theseus, gave a most disappointing audition, ignoring all the punctuation and breathing in all the wrong places – I can't understand how he's become a successful entrepreneur without having a clue about iambic pentameter! But neither am I totally convinced by his claims to mid-life sophistication and I fear he was only motivated by the hope of getting my signature on his petition against the return of Clive Horrobin.

So he could hardly expect me to accept his invitation to stage the production at Grey Gables any more than Sid Perks could hope that I would use the Bull – I can't risk being accused of nepotism as well as Political Incorrectness! Thank goodness I decided to look no further than my own garden at Ambridge Hall, the perfect setting for a magical lyrical comedy. In blank verse.

Auditions continued in the usual haphazard way, with only Nigel and Elizabeth showing any real fire and passion in their delivery of Oberon and Titania's quarrel scene – a little too much so, some might say! Bert got completely *au dessus de sa gare* as Bottom, and showed himself to be more literal than literary by questioning almost every line – I really can't have that sort of thing, and anyway, it's catching!

But Janet Fisher as Puck is a real find, though I had grave reservations about Trudy, who may see herself as Titania but comes across as Moll Flanders – I've offered her a walk-on fairy, instead. I don't want to crush her fragile psyche, and I've told her it *is* a crucial role – I think she believes me.

Of course, there are daily crises and irritations, like an invasion of bats in the garden – dreadful, 'Eldritch' creatures, diving about and ruining the audience ambience. (Robert must have built a bat box in the shrubbery.) The relief when Nigel and Elizabeth offered Lower Loxley as an alternative venue! I know Titania refers to bats as 'rere mice' with 'leathern wings'/To make small elves coats', but unless they could be trained to fly over to Lower Loxley and make a brief entrance, on cue, I don't know what earthly use they are.

Sean is thrilled by the design opportunity Lower Loxley offers, but I can't decide whether the text should be linear or curved in portrayal. To avoid confusing him further, I've told him I want grassy banks, a menacing forest and mist – lots of mist, to create the right magical somnambulism of the 'wood near Athens'.

Then came the discovery that Hayley, as Helena, and Kate, as Hermia, are the wrong way round – height-wise! I told Hayley to 'think short', nay 'diminutive', but she just looked at me blankly.

And no wonder, because at the next reheasal with Eddie (who was reading in for Roy as her lover, Lysander, and taking full advantage of his role) I noticed that she had shrunk to the correct height for the part merely by taking off her high heels! I never cease to be amazed by the seeming lack of sensitivity and intuition on the part of Ambridge players. But at that moment, as though in ironic echo of my thoughts, Laurence Lovell, of all people, slith- ered into the room, demanding to audition for Lysander. Someone in BADS

An early Ambridge Christmas revue.

or FLOS must have tipped him off about *The Dream* because he'd already been pestering me with messages and phone-calls and, though I had looked forward to giving him something insignificant to get his teeth into, I was forced to give him Theseus in desperation.

So I felt quite justified in reminding him that theatre may be an illusion, but no-one could be under any illusion about him being too old for Theseus, never mind Lysander! Moreover, that his mythical performance as the Red Shadow for the last hundred years was based on the fact that his face was almost entirely covered by a sort of yashmak, and he really should get a grip on himself!

I must say, I felt better after that, but I don't know how I'm going to break the news to Sean that we shan't be needing the hillocks I'd asked him to build, preferably on castors, for Kate to stand on in order to tower over Hayley in their scenes together. I'm not even sure where Kate is – I know she's been spending a lot of time on a protest to preserve the ancient lime trees from the widening of the Borchester bypass, although I'm not sure if I could face hanging out as a tree-dweller, especially with some of her strange friends. But I have got a petition going in tandem with my efforts on *The Dream*. And if I weren't so involved with *The Dream*, I'd probably be standing shoulder to shoulder with her, shifts permitting, at this very moment.

Positively thinking, *Dream*-wise, Phil Archer has promised to produce a tape of Elizabethan music and I think I've got Bert and Joe reasonably under control as Quince and Bottom. Plus, Jill Archer will make a fine Hippolyta, as long as she doesn't have a relapse and succumb to L. Lovell's overtures in the wings at the end of the play – Theseus and Hippolyta are supposed to be on honeymoon and LL isn't likely to miss such an opportunity! I'll probably need to have another quiet word with her.

The final casting is still open – well, it has to be, thanks to the actors' sense of commitment, which, in their case, they have not got! And I'm still worried about the men – in an emergency, like late harvest or broken-down tractors – but we're scheduled for early September if everything pans out.

Of course, Clive Horrobin might be coming back to the village (under a cloud, naturally) and while I can understand people's hostile feelings, it won't be easy for him. If the worst happened, I suppose I could always give him Flute depending on his questionable literacy levels. There might be a cast mutiny, but I'm sure Janet Fisher would back my gesture of using the Arts for the rehabilitation of felons. Or I might get him to help Sean backstage. In which case, maybe Nelson would consider Flute – he was a wonderful Ugly Sister, so he shouldn't have any problem cross-dressing as Thisbe when the mechanicals present *Pyramus and Thisbe* to Duke Theseus.

I keep telling myself that it'll be alright on the night. But so much depends on the success of *The Dream*. For instance:

1. It celebrates the Bardic influence on the artistic heritage of Ambridge and may set future expectations for the whole of Borsetshire.

2. It is a significant step for my personal credibility as an artistic innovator and theatrical impresario.

3. It marks my first decade in Ambridge as well as my significant birthday.

But, as Robert says, 'Lyndy, only *you* would take on something of this magnitude and only someone with your skills can make it work – and even if it doesn't, just remember, "The Show Must Go On!" And I'm off to nets – bye!'

How right he was. The show must go on and my mission is to see that it does. That mission will be accomplished.

This very wall was my model for the Pyramus and Thisbe scene in The Dream.

The French Connection

I'm not sure when I first became a Francophile, but I think it must have been some time during the Hundred Years' War and Shaw's *St Joan*. We were doing them for O Level and I remember being very impressed with Joan of Arc, or Jeanne d'Arc, or La Pucelle. I was getting a particularly hard time from the class bully – Angela Knotwell – and was badly in need of an heroic role-model who was as misunderstood as I. Joan of Arc seemed to fit the bill, since she managed to combine sensitivity with a down-to-earth approach and really inspired me to stand up for myself, though without having to resort to full armour and broad sword.

I couldn't wait to visit *nos cousins d'outre mer* on the school trip to Rouen and practise my conjugations on the very spot where my heroine had burnt to death. But on our arrival, we discovered that the only French spoken seemed to be of the rapid, non-O Level syllabus variety. I found I couldn't understand a word, so I spent most of the time wandering round the cathedral hoping to hear 'voices' (preferably in English) and eating *croque Monsieurs*. I failed French O Level, actually, but did spend six months as an *au pair* in Guernsey, where French is spoken, though mostly by the older inhabitants, who still seemed to be valiantly plotting ways of undermining the *Bosch*! However, I think that my occasional rendezvous with elderly fishermen telling of their daring wartime escapades in a sort of nautical French with Cornish overtones, probably advanced my quest for fluency, and I would certainly have no difficulty in laying mines or throwing hand grenades, should the need ever arise.

And then I managed to get another *au pairing* job with a family in Paris. I arrived just before Christmas, very broke, but wanting to take my hosts typically English gifts, so I raided my mother's 'Iron Rations' cupboard for supplies

This is one of my favourite portraits of Joan of Arc – before she had her hair cut.

of tomato ketchup, salad cream, baked beans, custard powder, fish paste, instant coffee, corn flakes and sliced, white bread. I popped in a small Christmas pudding (supermarket brand) and some evaporated milk, put everything into a plastic carrier bag decorated with gold tinsel and added a home-made card, shaped like a robin, saying *Joyeux Noel d'Angleterre*!

Imagine my horror when, upon opening this festive package, the entire family fell about, helpless with laughter, and unable to speak a word – for days, it seemed, unless you count – *'Les Anglais ha! ha! ha! – Typique! n'est-ce-pas?'* So I couldn't even build on the French I had learned in Guernsey, and I seriously toyed with the idea of applying for a crash course in mime at L'Ecole Marcel Marceau, as an *aide de communication*.

Thankfully, Robert and I have been popping across on day trips to Boulogne and even further inland (striking lorry-drivers permitting) for some

Brits invading a French market.

years, and with the occasional *Apprenons le Francais*! type of BBC course, I think I can honestly say that I feel confidently bi-lingual by now. Robert always says he's amazed at my courage – well, 'cheek!' is the word he uses – but I remind him that we would never have had the *Entente Cordiale* if someone hadn't been cheeky!

I have to say, that the idea of Town-Twinning Ambridge with Meyruelle – a village in the beautiful Languedoc area of South West France – was originally mine, even though Clarrie Grundy jumped on the bandwaggon after overdosing on Peter Mayle and pop singer Roch Voisine. But I am quite happy for her to demonstrate that even simple country folk can come up with sophisticated surprises in an attempt to broaden their often cramped horizons. Of course, it may have been part of her strategy to get Eddie to buy a farm in France, but as I could have told her, Eddie would be lost without his pint of Shires and meat pie and would merely mock *vin ordinaire avec brioche* as 'fancy foreign muck'!

Let us just say that, between us, Clarrie and I made the whole thing happen!

But what do we know of Meyruelle and how does it compare with Ambridge, heritage-wise?

Well, as we know, the French are happiest when they're fighting some-body – preferably the English. But having conquered us in 1066, taken over our land and infiltrated our language, they still weren't satisfied, and after much political inter-marrying between the two Royal houses, the balance of power was upset and led to what turned out to be, perhaps the longest GVR in history – internationally speaking – the Hundred Years War.

As if that wasn't bad enough, France also had to put up with the Wars of Religion. These were going on all over the place, but I think my favourite was centred in Languedoc and concerned the Cathars (from the Greek *katharos* – 'purified' and pronounced 'catarrh'!), who had very strong views on good and evil and held that the only way to overcome temptation was to live a pure, ascetic life, free from the materialism with which the Church was riddled at the time. They were horribly persecuted, fleeing to hilltop castles and holding out to the bitter, tragic end, and I think it's a great shame that they haven't had as much publicity as Joan of Arc, because they were every bit as brave and just as misunderstood – I thought so at fifteen and I haven't changed my opinion!

Well, I'm glad to say things have calmed down at last and Meyruellle has moved on from those bloody times to become a charming, peaceful place – though of course, I haven't actually been there, for reasons which are too embarrassing to disclose.

Suffice it to say, that ring-worm can strike anyone at any time, especially in the facial area, and although the French are notorious hypochondriacs and are morbidly well-informed on their own *sante*, I was simply not prepared to risk their unsympathetic response to my un-chic, though *recherché*, veil.

But as you might suppose, that did not stop my research into the village and its history and I have exposed some fascinating links with Ambridge – links of which I'm sure the *Meyruellois* are quite unaware.

To begin with, we know that Ambridge's earliest French connection was via the Fletchers (Archers) returning triumphant from doing a little post-war PR around Normandy, but it is unlikely that they would have ventured as far south as Meyruelle, preferring to stay near the coast, ready for a quick getaway when people got bored with their English ways.

However, by the time the French Revolution was raging, and the less fortunate *émigrés*, who had missed *le paquet* to Sunningdale, were seeking asylum in Ambridge, a certain 'aristo', le Duc d'Amboise, arrived at Brookfield farm claiming his inheritance: Ambridge's four mediaeval open fields – West Field,

Le Duc d'Amboise.

East Field, Lakey Hill and a field which I shall simply refer to as Anon, since I was unable to persuade anyone to enlighten me on its heritage, and I would hate to be accused of inventing material or including information from a dubious, even unauthenticated source.

Monsieur le Duc announced that his revered ancestor who had fought at Agincourt, had formed *un liaison* with one of the Fletcher's female camp-followers during the post-war rehab process, returned with her to Ambridge after the war and settled down as a tenant farmer, adopting the family name of Fletcher, while secretly retaining his noble title, d'Amboise – having his cake and eating it, one might say!

Monsieur le Duc also proclaimed that 'Ambridge' was merely the English corruption of 'Amboise', and that the land in question was rightfully his – '*Bien sur!*' Well, I'm sure you'll agree that that sort of behaviour is utterly *typique* and fools no-one. And you can imagine how he was sent packing by the Grundys with cries of, 'You oughta be ashamed! Coming over 'ere pretending to be a aristocrat, when really you're just another bloomin' Archer in disguise! Go on. Clear off back to the Loire Valley!'

Needless to say that, by now, the real Archers/Fletchers were suffering a severe identity crisis and felt it behoved them to keep a low profile, especially as they were supposed to be helping Lord Netherbourne in his attempts to 'Rescue an *Emigré*'.

But I feel sure they would have thanked the Grundys politely for getting them out of another fine mess, and might even have invited them round for a celebratory meal of faggots and brawn, with pease pottage on the side, washed down with gallons of home brew and followed by suet pudding and egg custard.

Of course, the Grundys would have to turn them down on principle, with remarks like, 'Keep your faggots and home brew. We got chitterlings and Kingston Black cider at 'ome, thank *you* very much! Anyhow, we got the Great Grundy Grudge to keep us going, so don't think you can get round us with your vile vittles!'

Of course, the history of Languedoc is much influenced by Celtic, Greek and Roman invasions and the many caves, or *grottes*, bear witness to prehistoric arts and crafts, not unlike those found in Ambridge, though I think the nearest thing you'd find to a cave would be the seasonal potholes in Phil Archer's lane. I have spoken to him about them and if a small child – e.g. young Pip – goes missing, he assures me that this will be the first place he will look.

But it is chiefly from Latin that the *Langue d'Oc* – the language of Southern France – evolved and was adopted by the troubadours, who practised the poetry of courtly love.

I attempted to discuss courtly love with M. Gustave Touvier, Mayor of Meyruelle, when he and Marie-Claire Beguet visited Ambridge for the town-twinning ceremony. I suspected that his knowledge of French was limited to the Languedocien dialect, because it was obvious that we weren't connecting, At least, not until he pinched my bottom. At first, I chose to interpret this gesture as a sort of cry for help – the naked desperation of one who lacks communication skills – until I noticed the disgusting way he was ogling Clarrie Grundy, and I was forced to conclude that the noble ethic of courtly love has become somewhat diluted over the centuries and now passes, ironically, as Gallic charm.

Clarrie has tried to do justice to Meyruelle in these photographs – and in some ways she has succeeded.

I am sorry to say that I am unable to give you a graphic description of Meyruelle, *elle-meme*, since most of Clarrie's well-intentioned snapshots amount to a few fuzzy close-ups of wine bottles, olives, a hoarding advertising Gaulois, sunflowers, the *mairie* – seen from the other side of the car park – and a blur of something mauve, which a Post Impressionist might label 'Lavender Field – Noon'. But at her insistence, and because I feel that one should encourage creativity in the visual arts, I have included some of her less esoteric work here.

So my own personal, but not uninformed, vision of Meyruelle, is of a sleepy jumble of red, pantiled roofs terracing a gentle hillside – not too steep, this is not a *village perché* and we are not in Peter Mayle country – clothed in vines, lavender and olive trees, with the occasional *pigeonnier*, originally designed to catch pigeon *guano* for making fertiliser, and now converted into *gites* by invading Brits, for making money! You are now in *la France profonde*!

I also see a *mairie* – every village, however small, must have one, it seems – and an *église*, sometimes large and looking rather neglected, but with a clock that is highly efficient and insists on striking the hour *and* all its quarters – twice, just in case you missed it the first time! No excuses for unpunctuality, but hell in the middle of the night! St Stephen's and its clock appear 'cute' in comparison.

There will be a *bar-tabac* – dark brown inside and smelling of Gitanes, where the local farmers hang out in blue overalls, drinking pastis and eating bread and cheese and olives. This is the closest the village comes to a cafe, with only three tables, and parasols that have seen better days, lurking outside on the path.

No-one says much, and if they do, it is always at the tops of their voices and with enormous kissing, hugging and slaps on the back, even though they only bumped into each other in the *boulangerie* five minutes earlier! I've often wondered why the French can be so tactile with each other and so distant with us, and I think it must be because they fear that lack of chic might be contagious. It's most noticeable in the way *douaniers* (passport control officers) handle your passport as though it were covered in – well, fish and chips!

Of course, Madame Clotilde, behind the bar, will be the mortal enemy of Pascal, *patron* of the rival hostelry on the edge of the village, with the racy reputation for being a sort of club known as *Le Chien et le Violon*. It is here that disgruntled males retreat when they have fallen out with Madame over the matter of the plastic wine *picher* with the slow leak, or the missing light bulb in the *toilette*, so vital if one is to avoid a watery death. And it is here that they can be a little *risqué* with Pascal's doxy, Aurore, the *femme fatale* of Meyruelle.

Actually, I was once considered to be the *femme fatale* of Ambridge, though I think I manage to look less of a cliché than Aurore, in her tight black top, tight red skirt, tight black tights and stilettos, and with occasional beret if she's just been to Mass. I daresay Mollie the Witch lured locals into the Cat and Fiddle wearing similar apparel all those years ago, though of course, in her case, the beret would have been a tall pointed hat, and she would have been returning from a Black Mass in Leader's Wood, probably astride a broomstick.

Sans doute, one will find Baggy and Snatch's equivalents – Jean-Christophe and Etienne – slumped over a *bier et brioche* under the poster of Juliette Greco or Johnny Halliday. Which is why, Clarrie told me stoutly, she resisted Gustav's pleas to '*Faites l'experience superbe d'Aurore!*' and insisted the Ambridge contingent should stick to the *bar-tabac*, so that together, she and Madame could swoon over the poster of their heart-throb, Roch Voisine!

The *boulangerie* will be quite modern: glass and chrome and concealed fluorescence and stacked with a log jam of baguettes of every length and thickness, along with *spécialités* like *pain d'olive* or *pain de pays* and amazing *patisserie*, laced with *cerises* or *abricots* and lashings of *crème fraiche*. There will also be butter, *confitures* (jams and preserves) honey, confectionery, maybe cheese and *saucisson*, but that's it! This is a *boulangerie*, not a *magasin*, so if you want massive

product choice with multi-brand options, and efficient customer-priority techniques, take your credit card and coolbox and drive 10 kilometres to the *hypermarché*!

M. le Boulanger will be deft of hand and neat of moustache, and as he flicks a coil of tissue-paper round your *ficelle*, and holds your gaze for just a half-second longer than necessary, you will feel like the only woman in the shop – as will the half-dozen other customers in the queue behind you.

I know Betty Tucker does her best, but frankly, in terms of customer service and *je ne sais quoi*, I don't think Ambridge has an equivalent to the *boulangerie* in Meyruelle. And it certainly doesn't have an equivalent to M. le Boulanger!

Leaving the *boulangerie*, you cross to Meyruelle's answer to Ambridge's village green *le piste* – a large, dusty, earthen area, shaded by lime trees, where the French national game of *boules* or *petanque* is played by men of all ages, with huge enthusiasm, even to the exclusion of darts, dominoes and angling, which they have left to the English! *Bien sur*! Yet another reason why the Grundy men could never settle in France.

However, in a burst of entreprenarial zeal, Sid and Kathy Perks staged a *boules* competition at the Bull recently, which attracted the entire Grundy clan's participation. Clarrie, looking *très sportive*, partnered Susan Carter in a successful fight to the finish against Robert and me – Robert, stylish as ever, could not yet quite master the Gallic swing! But Eddie Grundy, true to form, flew into a paddy when he lost, and hurled his *boule* at Joe, who ended up in casualty with a purple toe and no sympathy from anybody!

However, it seems that, having invested in the expense of building a *piste* (I should know – I had to cancel my verse-speaking workshop that evening, thanks to Jason on the pneumatic drill!), Sid is investigating how to join a League! A committee has been formed, a team name agreed – The Ambridge Bulls – and polo shirts, membership cards and subscriptions

decided upon. Fixtures are being set up, including a friendly match against The Fox at Edgeley, so I am hopeful that '*Boules* at the Bull' will become a valuable contribution to future intercourse with our friends in Meyruelle.

Opposite: Jean-Paul – ready for anything.

In fact, I believe there used to be a women's *boules* team in Meyruelle, but one can only suppose that M. Gustav Touvier had a hand in its sudden disbandment – all those bending *derrières* must have been too much!

The annual fete in Meyruelle is *nothing* like the village fete in Ambridge. I think this is because, although the village fete usually has the benefit of my bright ideas (this year saw me as the definitive fortune teller) and organisational skills, it never quite manages to be as smooth-running and professional as I would like. Something always goes wrong, or it rains, or both. Whereas the Meyruelle fete, which has absolutely no organisation or thought behind it, just seems to happen, with huge panache – music everywhere, , gypsies, animals and even a bull-run through the main street. Everyone drinks too much *vin ordinaire* and the sun always shines, and nobody would care if it didn't, which is, perhaps, the secret ingredient – plus being French, of course!

Which suddenly reminded me of Jean-Paul and his subtle hint to Robert about a GVR between his village and Meyruelle. Determined not to be put off by our sometimes erratic relationship, I ventured, during an off-peak hour, into the kitchen at Grey Gables to discuss this fascinating new development – the GVR *à la Francaise* – with Jean-Paul.

I reminded him of his remark *en passant* to Robert, that he wouldn't touch a pigeon shot by a filthy *Meyruellois* like Gustav Touvier *fils!*

He seemed pensive, then suddenly smiled and said, '*Alors! Pourqoui non?* I will tell you all, Mrs Snell!'

I listened, rapt, as he told me that his Tante Mireille came from the little-known hill village of Celeriac (pictured *right*), in the Dordogne, graced by a ruined castle and a vineyard, where the only form of entertainment, apart from smoking, drinking, eating etc, was playing boules. At one time, even the women had a boules team, outranking the men as reigning champions of the whole Dordogne – until the day they took on the Languedoc by playing an away match v. Meyruelle. Disaster struck in the shape of Gustav Touvier, pere, who, like his son, had a penchant for pinching.

The Celeriac team, captained by Tante Mireille, were furious and claimed it was not *très sportif* to sabotage their game by mounting a rear-guard action, though the Meyruelle team seemed momentarily gripped by Gustav's pincer-movement.

Naturellement, the game was abandoned, the Celeriac team took to their *charabanc*, the Meyruelle team disbanded itself *toute suite*, and a silent GVR has existed between the two villages ever since, aided by the fact that they are about a hundred and fifty miles apart.

I suggested that maybe Jean-Paul could find a window of opportunity, during the next Meyruelle visitation to Ambridge, to heal this tragic breach. After all, this had all happened years ago, and he didn't really know any of today's villagers. But he was adamant.

'*Non! Mrs Snell. Non! Non! Et Non!*' (Trust Jean-Paul to accentuate the negative when eliminating the positive.) 'I know everything about Meyruelle. Do I not know, "Like father, like son"? Have I not spoken with Clarrie? Have I not called a special pudding with her name? Have I not translated the love songs of Roch Voisine, for her alone? And have I not punched on the nose her jealous *salaud* of a husband, for doubting my honourable intentions to her? *Hein*? *Non*, Mrs Snell, it is over between Celeriac and Meyruelle, and I, Jean-Paul, will not betray the memory of

Tante Mireille and those gallant *femmes sportives*. *Adieu!*' And off he stalked, humming the *'Marseillaise'*!

I have to admit that he lost me halfway through this piece of rhetoric. He seemed to have stepped into a performance of something by Racine at *The Comedie Francais*. Though he *had* reminded me of Eddie's alarming over-reaction to his troubadour-like attempt to improve Clarrie's French comprehension. Received opinion suggests that it was Eddie who punched Jean-Paul first – much to Clarrie's mortification.

But I was most intrigued to know where exactly *is* Celeriac? My French atlas was most unhelpful – there was nothing remotely resembling Celeriac in the index, and a closer study of the Dordogne area drew a blank, so I can only suppose that it must have been one of the last remote Cathar strongholds – Jean-Paul had mentioned a ruined castle – and had been deliberately left off the map as a statement of – well, one wonders what! But it certainly throws a new light on Jean-Paul's fiercely independent spirit and explains why he is so stubborn and single-minded, let alone ready to punch people on the nose over a matter of honour.

However, our conversation made me realise the need to guard against the possibility of a GVR ever springing up between Ambridge and Meyruelle. The mere idea was too awful to contemplate! Nevertheless, I managed to, knowing that if I didn't, nobody else would. I was somewhat reassured to recollect that the first town-twinning visit of the French to Ambridge had, due almost entirely to my endeavours, been something of a success. In fact, a gentle scroll through my clipboard brought all those bitter-sweet memories flooding back.

Whoever had decided that the village fete should take place on the same day as my rehearsals for the community play – devised to entertain and inform the French visitors – had a lot to answer for! Despite my clearly worded rehearsal schedule, Martha Woodford refused to leave her fortune-teller's tent, saying she couldn't be in two places at once, so of course, the rest of the cast followed suit, leaving me to wait in vain in the village hall, wondering what had happened to loyalty, commitment and the British sense of fair play!

Well, by this time, I seemed, single-handedly, to have taken on the responsibility for the entire town-twinning event – I don't know what the committee thought they were supposed to be doing – and I found myself running around checking that Marjorie had got the Village Exhibition under way; explaining to George Barford that it was *de rigueur* for his welcome speech to be in French. I managed to calm him down by writing it out phonetically for him; bribing Kate Aldridge to proofread the Twinning Charter in exchange for a lift into Borchester and then sorting out the dyslexic calligrapher who couldn't even spell Ambridge correctly.

Then there was a whole morning spent persuading people to put up/with Meyruelle guests – I tried quoting the precedent set by Lord Netherbourne's 'Rescue an *Emigré*' campaign in 1793, in the hope of stirring British sympathy for the underdog. It also seemed sensible to check which hosts didn't mind having their mattresses hurled out of the window every morning for the customary French airing – but I explained that this *is* considered normal behaviour in France and would be a very nice gesture.

I think my stress levels peaked when Jennifer Aldridge refused to change, or even add to a single word of her script for the community play – writers are so proprietorial, I always find. And then Pat Archer suddenly decided to go on holiday, for some perverse reason and I was expected to take over the casting as well as rehearsals, which, considering there were several people I wasn't speaking to by this time, was particularly disagreeable.

However, the big day came, with all the usual last minute panics – sorting out the caterers, putting the last-minute touches to the Village Exhibition (Marjorie means well, but...), checking that the new road signs, 'Ambridge – Twinned with Meyruelle' were correctly spelt – once bitten, twice shy – and ready for installation at the four roads leading into Ambridge, immediately after the ceremony.

I think I can honestly say that my commentary, in French, guiding our guests through the cavalcade of Ambridge's heritage, as performed by David Archer, Kate and Debbie Aldridge, Martha Woodford and the rest of the cast, was the climax of the event. It meant a great deal to one to see the looks on those expressive French faces and I felt that my hours of practice, in front of the mirror in the Beige Boudoir, incorporating typical French gestures for added authenticity, were much appreciated.

Some residents of Meyruelle felt the need to wear Union Jack hats. Was this really necessary?

And what a *coup de théatre* to invite Henri Beguet, Marie-Claire's husband, to judge the Flower and Produce Show – I think he appreciated the attention after the way his wife had been flirting with Brian Aldridge.

In fact, I found Henri and I had quite a lot in common, since his father had been a member of the French Resistance movement, *le Maquis*, during the war; so at last, I had an opportunity to practise my explosive French vocabulary, which had lain dormant ever since Guernsey. I think he was quite impressed by my revelation that a *bombe surprise* was an elegant French pudding, not a weapon of ambush, but I was also able to exchange a few other points of *vocabulaire* with him. I pointed out that the English pudding gooseberry fool, made from sieved gooseberries and custard or cream, is so-called from the French *fouler* – 'to crush' – and has nothing to do with fool-ishness, unless you eat too much, of course, in which case, Jean-Paul might be tempted to subtitle it gooseberry cretin!

Henri also let slip that he was into ecology and gardening, so I amused him with a leguminous Trivial Pursuit teaser – *viz.* what well-known French dish is made with the following ingredients: *Lycopersicon esculentum, cucurbita pepo, capsicum annuum, allium cepa* and *solanum melongena?*

Without batting an eyelid, he replied, '*Alors, c'est le ratatouille, n'est ce pas?*' My turn to be impressed! But then, he is a smallholder and has a regular stall at the market in Meyruelle, neatly sited between Hippolyte, on the chilled cheese van, and Honorine, the *friperies et brocante* lady, who is also his mistress – apparently! Aghast, I immediately checked that Marie-Claire was out of earshot, but he didn't seem bothered and asked me who *I* was having an affair with 'Eddie Grundy, *peut-etre?*'!

I implored him to keep his voice down, and hotly denied such a prepos-terous idea, but he said it was *pas de probleme*, because Gustav had already told him that I was the *femme fatale* of Ambridge, and had I thought of having an affair with Jean-Paul? He continued this unsolicited dissertation on *liaisons dangereuses*, by informing me that he suspected Jean-Paul of having had affairs with both Clarrie and Caroline, probably at the same time, but that in France this was *normale*! Nevertheless, was this not the moment for me, '*La belle* Lynda,' to dissipate the *ennui* of Jean-Paul by showing him my charms?

I, *au contraire*, felt that it was the moment to change the subject to some-thing manageable, so on a more serious note, I asked if he would like my special French cure for bee-stings, which one must find a hazard when one is gathering the above-mentioned vegetables from one's market garden.

He said, '*Alors, moi, je fais un pi-pi sur la piqué et le frappez bien! Hein?*' A trifle crude, I know, especially when accompanied by graphic gestures, but spoken with such charm, that I almost *didn't* offer him my Gallic alternative.

Except that I felt it safer to keep him to the market garden, in case he digressed back to the bedroom.

He listened patiently to my more sophisticated remedy, as follows:

Blend one wineglass of Beaume de Venise with two garlic cloves;
place on a poultice of vine leaves and crushed olive stones;
apply to sting and secure with length of baler twine.

And then he said wasn't it time I took him to the Beige Boudoir to show him my *bateau lit* – he was feeling homesick!

But, *Dieu merci,* I was suddenly summoned to 'Refreshments' to explain to the French that quiche in English, means – well, something else. But I don't think they bore any hard feelings, and I noticed them settling for sausages on sticks and trifle.

Thus it was, that by following my tried and true principle of learning from other people's mistakes, I was able to save the day.

But I am sorry to have to report that after all my zeal and initiative on that occasion, I was not even informed by the committee when plans for a return delegation from Ambridge to Meyruelle were under way.

I was hurt, but not surprised. I know what short memories people have about one's past achievements, and if they think they can action, unaided, one of my proven successful *modus operandi* – then fine! I would have had to do all the talking, anyway – they haven't got a word of French between them!

Which is why I offered to give French lessons at a mere £5 per person, per hour. I put posters up with Jack Woolley's approval, but when I announced my modest fee at the first lesson – to Clarrie and one or two others – there were sharp intakes of breath all round and the level of enthusiasm went down like a lead balloon.

Jean-Paul bravely samples an English trifle.

However, we struggled through the basics for a while, with Jack Woolley doing his best, against all the odds, and he was the only one to turn up to the next lesson. I couldn't deny feelings of rejection and Robert said that maybe the ringworm attack was an act of God – at least I could withdraw with dignity behind my veil. But I think it will be some time before I offer my services in the bilingual department again. And I'm quite sure Jean-Paul is unlikely to offer his!

But I feel that I can't leave the subject of the 'French Connection' without revealing my own personal tribute to French cuisine and to Jean-Paul and his distinctive Cathar heritage. It is still in the development stage, but I would like to think that, in some small way, it might make up to him for William Grundy trying to sell him garden snails! And who knows, he might even interpret it as one of my 'charms'.

Blackberry.

A Walk on the Wild Side

Selected seasonal jottings from my random rural rambles

I now offer the visitor a pot pourri of the delights available to the wildlife enthusiast, in and around Ambridge, drawn from my own experience as a supporter of the RSPB, Plantlife, BET, CPRE (Council for the Preservation of Rural England), Nature Conservancy, The Wildlife Trust, the Green Party and many others too numerous to mention!

Come with me behind the charming facade of this rural scene and experience the heights and depths, the agony and the ecstasy, the tragedy and bathos of Nature's 'Theatre of the Spectacular'! Why not carry these handy jottings with you, as you wander the woodlands and meadows – always following the signposted footpaths, of course! Who knows, you may be able to add your own thoughts and discoveries, further enriching our rural heritage thereby.

Autumn
Season of mists and mellow fruitfulness,
Close-bosom friend of the maturing sun. (Keats)

September 10th
Robert and I set off after church to trace route of Eadric's/Eddie's Ditch, with view to claiming as footpath, also to keep Joe Grundy sweet – for any future needs. All that remains is rutted tractor track – disgraceful! NB definitely add

to list of future campaigns with priority status. Horrified to find old beer can containing trapped hedgehog – known locally, and Bardically, as urchins – trying to hibernate. Spines got jammed when tried to back out. Very distressed, but *not* case for St Tiggywinkle's, The Wildlife Hospital Trust, mercifully. Back home, built dedicated hibernation heap in hosta bed, providing enough leaves to protect from cold, but not to make him breathe faster – might use too much energy. Hostas should also attract endless supply of inebriated slugs from yoghurt-pot beer traps. He soon settled, yawning at thought of winter sleep, safe from martyrdom in bonfire – maybe taste of alcoholic slugs will encourage him to stay permanently to prevent martyrdom of hostas! NB check village bonfires for hibernating hedgehogs, Nov 5th early a.m., before too late!

Alcoholic connections with Joe Grundy's charming story of badgers ('sellers' in dialect) seen wobbling drunkenly around orchard after eating his Laxton Superbs. Supposedly due to dry summer – ground too hard for them to get at worms etc., apples fermented in stomachs – same with pigs, when allowed into orchard. Robert said more likely to have been Joe '*Seeing* badgers and pigs' when under influence of his Kingston Black cider. R. can be very cynical sometimes.

September 15th

Chatting to Marjorie A. outside St S's at lunch time – sudden flock of house martins departing nests in church eaves for journey south to Africa, via France and Spain. NB check with Gustav in Meyruelle for sightings of resting birds *en voyage*.

Thrilled to see late spotted flycatcher ('hewsick') grasp drowsy wasp by head end and deftly wipe body to and fro on twig to shed sting and remove poison – brilliant! Applied this method to wiping mud off wellies on 5-bar gate leading out of churchyard. Disaster! – gate swung back, taking welly with it. Left up to ankles in sockful of mud! Nature knows best! QED.

September 29th

Michaelmas Day: Cycling past churchyard, waved to Bert, tidying waist-high Michaelmas daisies! Headed for serious blackberrying session along Ambridge hedges – visitors advised never be without suitable receptacle when on village walkabout. About 400 micro-species of blackberry in Britain – tips of tender, new shoots used to be picked and eaten by children at turn of century. Much country lore on subject e.g. today last day for picking before Devil taints berries; kittens born in September 'blackberry kittens' – small, weak and mischievous; crawling under a bramble hoop brings luck at cards, cures rickets, whooping cough, boils and blackheads. No intention of putting to test, but managed to gather several pounds for pies, jams and, as special treat, blackberry wine. Robert said, 'I don't mind Elderflower Petillant, Lyndy, but do we really need blackberry *wine* when we've still got plenty of good French red that you laid down on my birthday that year – what's wrong with that?' Didn't bother pointing out that according to Jilly Goolden *et al.*, most red wine tastes of blackberries anyway, so with luck, he won't spot difference.

October 15th

While doing feasibility study on Aethelwold's Hedge for future campaign – also with priority status re Joe Grundy, as above – discovered twigfuls of clustered hibernating ladybirds. In Middle Ages known as Beetle of Our Lady, but in France, *bête à Bon Dieu*, the good God's animal; in Germany, *Marienkafer*, Mary's beetle; in Spain, *Mariquita*, Little Mary, etc. Dread to think what Eurobeetle equivalent title the EU will come up with eventually! Closer observation revealed them to be rare, white, aphid-/mildew-eating *Thea 22 punctata* – white wing case with 22 spots! Can't think how these could have escaped my 'Ladybird Spot-Counting' campaign some years ago, but valuable find. Gently removed some into handkerchief and transferred to my *Rosa* 'Zephyrine Drouhan' – notorious martyr to mildew – to hibernate and perform double duty next summer.

Crocus nudiflorous.

October 20th

Found enchanting, and quite rare form of wild autumn crocus, *Crocus nudiflorous*, nestling in grass halfway up Lakey Hill. Not native, but brought back by Knights of St John, returning from Crusades, who set up crocus farms for its cheap saffron substitute. Used for dye, medicine and flavouring – reason birds always demolish garden varieties! Grows in poor soil, unlike native *Colchium autumnale*.

Rob said: 'Would it hurt to dig up just one, to give to Grundys – it would do well in their poor soil and they could start a saffron-growing self-help scheme and make some money, like their forefathers.'

Appalled! Rob knows perfectly well digging up wild plants absolutely *verboten* – not only by me – by law! Bad enough that so many *Galanthus elwesii* (snowdrops) already threatened with extinction in Turkey, because illegal collection and sale. How would he feel if never saw another 'Crowd of golden daffodils' in Leader's Wood, because some greedy, unenlightened person had dug all up to sell at car boot sale? Besides, only money Grundy forefathers ever made was in Grange Farm Gnomes, and enough said on *that* subject!

He said, 'Sorry, it was a momentary slip – I was only trying to be helpful. And why are you talking in *précis*?'

Felt slightly abashed; decided to make usual allowances.

October 31st

Commandeered John and Hayley to help check village bonfire for stray hedgehogs. Some reluctance, until promised them special culinary surprise. Twenty hedgehog-free minutes later, delivered *coup de grace* – bright orange pumpkin – 'Spellbound' variety, harvested that morning.

Surprised that they didn't know history of fascinating vegetable, so informed them pumpkin derived from Latin *pepo*, later known as pompon or pompion from French. Pilgrim Fathers first celebrated Thanksgiving for safe arrival in America with pumpkin pie – even had law to cut hair short around dried pumpkin shell placed on heads – hence New Englanders nickname 'Pumpkin-Heads'.

At which Hayley looked meaningfully at John, who looked threatened – not amused! Silence. Finally, 'Roight! Well, thanks very mooch, Leenda – that was reeelly eenterestingg. Actchallay, we were planningg a Hallowe'en lantern, weren't we, John? Thees'll look smashinggg all hallered owt, loike. Coom an, John, let's get scoopingg!'

I know Hayley doesn't speak the local dialect, but one sometimes feels she might just as well! Only hope Pat manages to rescue pumpkin innards to make delicious soup/pie/jam, or at least plant seeds for new crop to sell in farm shop – some good may yet come out of all this!

Winter

When icicles hang by the wall,

And greasy Joan doth keel the pot. (The Bard)

November 20th

Bitterly cold sub-zero today. Noticed swan trying to push against ice on Am to reach mate on other side. Threw crumbs to help keep its energy up, but water vole grabbed them! Oh dear! – really *not* a rodent person – haven't forgiven them for bringing Black Death to Ambridge in 1349, *or* suffering embarrassment of mice in cellar and rat gate-crashing New Year's Eve party at the Hall. Rob's comment – 'Get a cat!' – hardly helpful, because not cat person, either.

However, considered Bard's words:

> *There be land rats and water rats,*
> *Land thieves and water thieves. (Hamlet)*

and cheered up at thought of dear Ratty in *Wind in the Willows* diligently clearing invasive weed from water channels, but now, sadly under threat from invading mink – sort of anti-social super-ferret, breeding like mad. Memo: don't mention mink-breeding to Grundys – could result in more dead turkeys at Christmas!

Hermes hell-bent on strange encounters with ice on river – strange encounter for me too, if I had to rescue him! Managed to restrain on lead – tragic accidents occur too easily to heroic animal lovers. Memo: put up notices on trees nearby, 'Remember – Leads Save Lives!'

Checked river for herons, after hearing Tom F's horror story of birds frozen into ice and breaking their legs – terrible! Noticed frozen fox tracks leading to water's edge – might only get few drops, but thank goodness Ambridge isn't Africa, where could get dragged underwater by crocodile – according to Sir David Attenborough *et al.*, anyway.

Irresistible robin in alder tree establishing territory in song, listening out, ready to defend to death. Despite warlike tendencies, robin known for social skills e.g. in *The Secret Garden*, a Robin helped Mary find hidden garden. Threw some striped sunflower seeds – always carry bagful on winter walks to avoid repeat of winter 1947, when many birds frozen dead on branches.

Met Edward Grundy Jnr. also on way to feed birds, offered him some seed, but said he preferred his own, home-made mixture of chopped worms and sliced slugs. Suggested birds didn't need *that* sort of help – he said he was practising dissection for biology lessons next term! He offered me some for 30p a handful! It must run in the family!

December 12th

Wandered down to Leader's Wood to check on Wild Service Tree – still there! Also cork oak Tom F connects with witches – now draped in mistletoe! Amazing sacred/profane history, i.e. known as all-heal against poison, thunder/lightning and said to increase fertility – hence, 'Kissing Bough'. But never welcome inside churches – suggestion that because wood may have

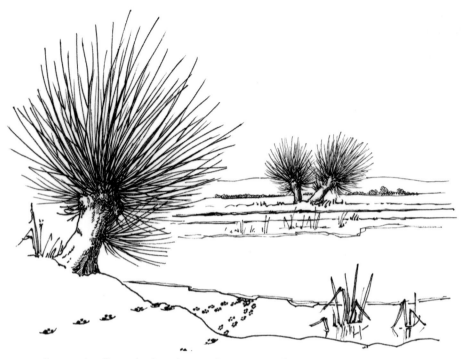

been used to make Cross, it shrank to twiggy proportions out of shame.

Remembered *Plantlife Survey* records apple trees as most popular mistletoe host (also lime and poplar) – maybe Joe G would donate some mistletoe berries from his apple orchard to plant in my old Bramley.

At Grange Farm, found Joe chasing ferret out of turkey shed (*knew* I was right about not mentioning mink!) He said mistletoe grew too high up to reach, and would have to employ ancient tradition of blasting a clump down with shotgun! – At cost of 10p per shot, because his aim not as good as once was!

Decided not to risk fatal accident in apple orchard and declined, but will hope that passing mistle thrush may do job for me.

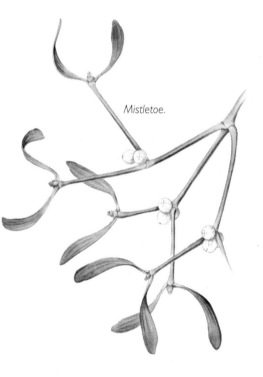

Mistletoe.

December 20th

Found rather boring berryless holly – birds need berries more than I do – but wonderful ivy berries to paint red. Will probably use *Aucuba japonica 'Maculata'* and Pyracantha to augment.

Memo: collect alder and pine cones to spray gold for effective festive recycled decorations.

Also, keep sprig of holly to pop into Aga on Shrove Tuesday – gives certain *je ne sais quoi* to pancakes, according to Susan Carter, who is showing signs of *haute cuisine*, if not *haute couture* – at last!

Pine cones and alder cones.

Aucuba japonica 'Maculata'.

January 10th

Suffering severe bout of post-Christmas blues, plus SAD, plus news of decision *not* to send proceeds from pantomime to Rain Forest Appeal – when spotted first snowdrops tucked under Marjorie A's hedge – nearly fell off cycle with sudden thrilling question, 'If winter comes, can spring be far behind?'

Heaps of black soil on snow in churchyard – moles busy, even now. They overcome rigours of winter by keeping larder of spare worms which they disable with nip to head end, so keeping fresh and tasty when needed. Name from Saxon: 'molde' – earth, and 'warpen' – to throw. Known collectively as a labour of moles – certainly labour-intensive to keep at bay!

Pyracantha.

January 20th

Concerned by yet more of Tom's tales of Winter 1947 – barn owls huddled together for warmth by day – most unusual! Telephoned sundry farmers offering to come and distribute suitable owl food around their barns. Only response from Ruth Archer – polite, but cool reminder that since owls are carnivores, did I propose to leave bits of raw meat lying around to attract rats? Mortified! Know perfectly well what birds of prey eat – since discovering Montagu's harrier! Rang back and left informative message that was planning to unearth a few overwintering molluscs which might tempt owls, defy rats and possibly interest insomniac hedgehogs! Unfortunately, no molluscs available because of rock-hard ground – now know how birds feel – and hedgehog must have removed those under pots on patio.

January 31st

Thank goodness for thaw! But remembered frost hollow at my Country Wildlife Pond on Aldridge Estate. Delighted to find William Grundy already there, gently melting remaining ice with hot water from Thermos flask – explained to me that breaking ice sends harmful shock waves down to frogs overwintering in mud below. Churlish to tell him I already knew this – congratulated him on excellent green attitude and *pour encourager*, gave him bag of sunflower seeds which he immediately devoured – not what I meant at all – that was not it at all!

Spring

And in green underwood and cover
    Blossom by blossom the Spring begins. (Swinburne)

February 2nd, Candlemas Day

Very mild for February – can spring be far behind? Met Phil Archer strolling up Lakey Hill – gloomily predicting return of cold weather 'any day now' – typical farmer! Ignored him and gulped in lungfuls of good spring air.

February 10th

Ventured out for first time since struck down with dreadful cold on Candlemas Day – weather suddenly turned bitter. Terrible hacking cough reminiscent of Joe G's Farmers' Lung – panicked and sent Rob down to Grange Farm for advice. Clarrie produced following alternatives:

1. Bag of goose grease and/or bacon fat worn round throat;
2. Horse liniment rubbed into throat and chest;
3. 'Or you could try badger fat, Mr Snell – that's best, according to Joe, and he should know! But you wanna be careful – it's ever so strong. He says it'd melt a tin can, so he keeps his in a bottle. He told me it's the fat scraped from glands at the base of the badger's tail – I told him not to be so 'orrible! But he swears by it, so you might as well have a try – 'ere y'are.'

Though never actually uncorked bottle, smell seemed to seep through glass. Imagination reeled with hideous visions of badger-baiting – long since stamped out – so exactly how *old* was the badger's fat? It was all too unthink-

able! Said to Rob, 'To open that bottle would be like opening Pandora's box!' He said, 'Lyndy, you're delirious – get under this towel and inhale this steaming bowl of wholesome Friar's Balsam – you'll soon feel better!' Rob always so practical and such comfort when old country habits get too much for one.

Cold snap hadn't deterred clumps of early daffodils and primroses under Ancient Brookfield Hedge, which now showing much dead wood in need of clearing. NB enquire re courses on hedge-laying, tree-planting etc.

Also noticed used bits of baler twine scattered about on Ancient Hedge – collected these up to present to Phil A later, plus strong words on threat to wildlife and evils of sloppy husbandry. Early hours – heard blood-curdling scream of fox calling. Next morning found remains of rabbit on lawn – Oh dear! – 'Nature, red in tooth and claw' (Tennyson).

February 12th

Saw Phil A walking his land – challenged him with now neatly rolled-up baler twine from pocket of thorn-proof – he was furious! Said he'd used it to mark parts of hedge where dead wood needed clearing. Offered to mark them for him, using attractive, green plant ties – so much more discreet. He said, 'I thought discretion was supposed to be the better part of *valour*, not *hedge maintenance!*' – and walked off in huff! He's obviously in denial – will continue to try to get him to own the problem – as discreetly as possible, naturally.

March 5th

New leaf buds appearing everywhere and 'bright' smell in air. Charming young lovers, John and Hayley, strolling hand in hand through churchyard, closely followed by Bert – 'They're still at it!' he hissed. Eventually realised he meant moles – piles of soil all over place – Bert getting desperate! Suggested he sinks bottle into mole run – wind blowing across neck produces low whistle to scare them. He said, 'Yes, but – I reckons t'wouldn't only be the moles who'd be scared – some very superstitious folk in the neighbourin' vicinity – believe all sorts of rubbish about "Ghosties and Ghoulies", don't they?' Gave me very strange look, which I parried with, 'Have you heard of the mole *cricket*, Bert? Lives just below soil surface in damp meadows and *churchyards*, so-called because has big spade-like front legs and *burrowing* habit – eats leather-jackets and cutworm caterpillars?'

Snowdrop.

His strange look became one of panic, as hurried off to Bull, presumably on bottle hunt to action my suggestion, or maybe for comforting pint of Shires. Didn't bother to tell him that mole cricket on decline – he's suffered enough, despite his impertinent innuendoes, which will overlook, for now.

March 18th

Saw two March hares having ball in winter wheat – quite Antipodean in movements – unlike rabbits – so intelligent – would probably box fox's ears! Dear little lambs everywhere, quite hysterical in movements, with similar IQ to rabbits, probably destined for Jean-Paul's culinary intervention, though blissfully innocent of fact. Question: If the French were sentimental re animals, would *levraut farci beauval* and *agneau ambassadrice* ever have been invented? Discuss, with reference to the disturbingly *farouche* nature of these dishes, in the context of events leading up to the French Revolution.

Rooks' nests in copse looking quite precarious – not very attractive birds – once considered as much a nuisance as rats – hence old Rook and Rat clubs to deal with them by paying few pence per corpse – simple initiative, maybe worth reviving for licensed gun holders. NB check with G. Barford.

March 26th

Lady Day: strange – no sign of farmers rushing out to pay annual rents! Coppiced willows – *Salix britzensis* – creating haze of yellow/red, once used for making 2 metre poles – hence measurement a 'pole'. Not many people know that nearby fairy ring toadstools have v. intimate relationship with trees, i.e. fungi's underground threads absorb high-energy sugars from roots of partner plants (Willow) in exchange for absorbing water and essential minerals to benefit host. Shared fungal theory with Pat Archer, when called into farm shop for 3 carrots and a parsnip. 'Sorry, Lynda – the only fungi I'm interested in are mushrooms, and we don't grow 'em, we just sell 'em – anything else?'

As withdrew to cram purchases into cycle basket, she called, 'Why not tell Peggy and Marjorie all this? They're into mushroom gathering, especially in wee, small hours! But don't tell Joe! Ha! Ha! Ha!' Decided to ignore this veiled reference to Joe Grundy threatening these two interlopers with shotgun, when found gathering early morning mushrooms on his land – can't imagine why! All very undignified, but surprised that Pat so insensitive about mother-in-law Peggy's behaviour – although …!

Much gratified to see wooden Finger Posts surviving well. So important for ramblers and tourists alike to know where they are, since locals erratic in communicating accurate info. But village pond very disappointing – melted ice revealed choked with weed and certain unmentionable objects, of organic *and in*organic nature! Will consider organising 'Dredge and Dispose' working party, but only if Sean sets up several skips – he is a builder, after all. Possibly worth importing few remaining water voles to keep pond weed-free? Second thoughts – bad idea – in view of existing bad press re Black Death, could be wrongly accused of bringing Weil's Disease to Ambridge.

Summer

Sumer is icumen in.
> *Lhude sing cuccu!*
> *Groweth sed and bloweth med*
> *Ande springth the wude nu* (Anon. 13th century)
> (In the original Middle English, actually!)

May 12th

Heard first cuckoo this morning! NB inform *Times* asap. Wonderful sunshine – at last! All footpaths brimming with hawthorn blossom and dog roses – heavenly fragrance!

Spent morning in Leader's Wood gathering armfuls of bluebells, felt like one of those romantic paintings on front of tasteful greeting card. No question of digging up – too invasive for garden anyway – look v. elegant in white vase with pink home-grown tulip 'Apricot Beauty'. Also spotted Montagu's harrier – saved from crop-sprayer – now happily regurgitating bits of indeterminate mammal, probably rabbit, into gaping beaks of young. No signs of twitchers – amateur bird-watchers – also clamouring for attention, but must exercise vigilance.

On rabbit theme, Queendown Warren, Kent, once farmed as rabbit warren for Queen Eleanor of Provence in 13th century, because had passion for rabbit pie – presumably with a delicious *sauce avignon-naise* of cream, olives and tarragon!

May 28th

Sudden thought that Queendown Warren also boasts many wild orchids, reminded to rush down to country pond for progress report on wild orchid I discovered there some years ago. Other orchids are 'pyramid' and 'man' – which looks like gallows from which a number of green men are being hanged – really quite attractive – not a bit bloodthirsty! Had to lie down in grass to find my orchid, which now has couple of seedlings – more monitoring for next season!

May 29th

Oakapple Day in the Country Calendar and My Birthday – my *demi-siecle* actually! And as Lupton said in *A Thousand Notable Things* (1597):
> *If you take an Oak apple from an Oak Tree, and open the same,*
> > *you shall find a little worm therein*
> > *Which if it doth flye away, it signifieth warres*
> *But if it do creepe about, it betokeneth scareceness of corn*
> > *and if it run about, it forshoweth the plague.*
> (Seems you just can't win with an oak apple!)

Felt fairly safe wearing traditional oak-leaf wreath I'd made to breakfast. Rob said, 'Happy Birthday, darling – What's that on your head?' Explained – but he said, '*Promise* you won't wear it to work.' Much discussion. Finally agreed to edit wreath down to bracelet size.

At Grey Gables, found anonymous birthday gift on Reception desk – *no card*. Opened it to discover attractive plant *Soleirolia soleirolii* – otherwise known as Mind-your-own-business! – very depressing start to birthday, but think I have unravelled mysterious source. Mr Woolley said, 'Happy Birthday, Lynda! Oh dear! Why are you wearing that herbal poultice? Have you hurt your wrist? I mean, I know you're very medically minded – I still haven't got over you giving me the kiss of life when I had my heart attack – but don't you think you might be better off with one of Peggy's elastic bandages?' Declined, but removed oak-apple bracelet anyway, to avoid it catching in keyboard.

Now paying price for orchid enthusiasm yesterday – had to pass field of oil-seed rape on way home – now in depths of severe hay-fever attack! Dreadful plant! Such a common colour, especially compared with delicacy of cowslip, which I'm sure it usurped. No doubt wretched pollen beetle heading for Ambridge gardens to attack and destroy – still no eco-friendly control. I'm sorry, but afraid I'd be happy with *any* kind of control!

Sought relief under large sun hat and veil in low-allergen garden – stayed there until got eaten alive by mosquitoes homing in from marshy river garden – finally retired to bathroom, washed off oil of citronella (*supposed* repellent, but not for *me, hélas!*) Then chivvied Rob to get *accoutred* for our appearance as 'Alderman and Goodwife Snell' at traditional Oak Apple Feaste at Bull – Sid's latest people-puller and my birthday treat. Rob looking very seventeenth century in plum velvet and ruffled lace – my creation. I almost underwent embarrassing pannier panic-attack in Hassett Room doorway, but survived to enjoy delicious mulled wine etc. Back home, cuddled up to Rob under mosquito net, to read Rob's birthday present, *Travels with my Goat* by a nomad of the Nubian Desert, as told to Kate Adey.

June 18th

Persuaded Rob to come wild-food foraging through ancient woodland – reminding him that Bard had already given permission:

> *Powerful grace that lies*
> *In herbs, plants, stones, and their qualities:*
> *For naught so vile that on the*
> *earth doth live*
> *But to the earth some special*
> *food doth give.*

Rob reluctantly agreed to carry baskets and bags – as long as nobody saw him! In two hours had collected broom flowers (*above*), red & white clover, rose bay willow herb, wild garlic and dandelion leaves – will all spice up summer salad. Also wood sorrel for salt and vinegar flavour, and elder flowers to cook in light batter, and young nettle tips for soup. Rob got stung by nettles – became tired and emotional – won't ask him again!

Arrived home and transformed whole collection into delicious meal of nettle soup, followed by organic salad with home-made goat's cheese, followed by wild strawberries (*right*) and Bridge Farm yoghurt (peach flavour), accompanied by bottle of Elderflower Petillant. Rob woke in night – raided larder for organic oatcakes and Pru Forrest's rhubarb and blackcurrant jam (I'd been saving that as possible investment!) then lay awake complaining of nettle rash, while I lay awake wondering if I'll ever make countryman of Rob. Would inviting Bert F to dinner help? And would he

expect steak and kidney pie, rather than organic salad, thus confusing Rob with mixed message? Clearly not enough just to play cricket with David Archer, Tony Archer *et al.*, in hope something will rub off.

Brain in overdrive, fresh crop of mosquito bites throbbing and Rob mumbling, 'That's the last time you'll ever get me to go out in shorts.' Finally fell asleep at 3.30 a.m. – woken by dawn chorus at 4.00 a.m. – a perfect summer day!

June 20th

Midsummer's Eve – always a Bardic time! Found romantic hypericum, St John's Wort, growing in churchyard, awash with yellow flowers – very significant because legend is that if young girl keeps a flower in hanky, her future husband will take it from her at Christmas.

Checked out with Bert. 'That's right – another story says that if a girl fasts all day, then sits in the church porch on Midsummer's Eve, she'll see her husband to be. That's how I met my Freda – she were just coming out the church porch with her friends, all giggling like, and I was on me way home with me mates, after an evening at the Bull, and we kinda – merged, like. They were all carrying St John's wort in their hankies an' all – not taking no chances! There musta been about six weddings that Christmas!' Informed Bert of romantic plant's healing properties *viz.* John Gerard, famous herbalist, described its 'oile of the colour of bloud, which is a most pretious remedie for deep wounds.' Also makes good throat gargle and recently found to contain antidepressant more effective than modern drugs, but suggested Bert didn't try to make herbal preparation himself, because also contains some poisonous compounds. He said why would he do that – he wasn't depressed, 'excluding moles, o'course!'

At dusk, Rob and I, in romantic mood, ventured up Lakey Hill in hope of hearing nightingale – no hope of hearing cuckoo – they go on strike after Midsummer's Eve. Air heavy with metal, honeysuckle and other unidentifiable perfume, as Kate Aldridge and friends drooped around bonfire in Druidic mode, 'Yeah, it's a sort of solstice thing, Lynda, you know, midsummer rituals – wild!' Rob said, 'Let's get out of here, before the police arrive!' Arrived home around midnight to hear nightingale, at last, in garden – heavenly!

St John's Wort.

> *. . . a year ago, or less than twain,*
> *No finches were, nor nightingales,*
> *Nor thrushes,*
> *But only particles of grain,*
> *And earth and air, and rain.* (Hardy)

July 15th

St Swithin's Day. Kindest thing to say about today is that rain is needed for fruit harvest – old saying, 'St Swithin is christening the little apples.'

Met Brenda Tucker in churchyard collecting wildflowers for Flower Festival before Bert's scythe got them. Said poppies her favourite – told her that red poppies said to grow in places where blood shed e.g. fields around Penny Hassett where Battle of Hassett Bridge saw fall of many Roundheads and Royalists. Brenda said she 'hadn't got to that in History yet,' but in view of all the poppies, there must have been a mega battle in St Stephen's churchyard! Explained that poppy seeds carried there by wind – so no connection. Don't think she believed me. Obviously hadn't got to wind propagation in Natural History.

July 27th

V. concerned to see so much giant hogweed (*Heracleum giganteum*) invading roadside verges. Handsome, statuesque, but contains blister-producing sap if scarred – v. painful reaction. Can disperse 50,000 seeds per year along linear corridors e.g. verges and rivers, choking out other native plants and endangering public health.

Donned mask, goggles, wellies and gardening gauntlets as protection against deadly sap, and attacked verges along Lower Loxley Road. Met Jennifer Aldridge who laughed and said, 'I thought you liked cow parsley, Lynda – you've always shown such interest in that patch in Martha's garden.'

Declined to reveal supernatural truth re Martha's cow parsley and explained that we were not talking about mere cow parsley here. JA quite indignant,

Giant hogweed.

Poppies.

'But I planted *Heracleum giganteum* for architectural interest in my south-facing border last year – looks wonderful beside the *Agave americana* – so sculptural!' (But unlikely to survive winter unless trussed up with hessian to resemble cross between scarecrow and tepee.)

'I'm sure Brian would rather you pulled up ragwort instead – it's poisonous to animals, you know.' (Yes, I *do* know actually. Once chastised JG for ripping up pretty wildflower which turned out to be ragwort – humiliating.) Almost tempted to remark that Brian quite expert on flora – especially Mind-your-own-business, but remembered his wildlife open day and relented.

August

Saw vixen leading cubs into corn stubble to forage around. In old days, hounds loosed into field after them – known as cubbing – way of teaching hounds difference between farm animals and fox prey.

Slight scent of changing season in air – leaves looking dusty, beginning to turn gold. Cygnets on Am looking quite grown-up, also changing colour. Water covered in awful green weed – only happened in last couple of years. Good remedy is to remove with old loo-brush, kept for purpose, of course.

Ragwort.

Everyone getting ready for Flower and Produce Show – air rich with seasoned fruits and seasoned rivalries!

For me, that's one of the wonders of Nature – that she has a short memory. She forgets the successes and failures from year to year, and starts each season as though it were the very first – fresh and full of hope – as at the very beginning of Time! As Gerard Manley Hopkins once observed:

> *Nature is never spent;*
> *There lives the dearest freshness deep*
> *down things …*

No further argument necessary to encourage us to strive to conserve such wonders!

Epilogue

Well, I hope you have enjoyed this illuminating little excursion behind the scenes of Ambridge. Who knows, I may have extended your horizons with a few illuminating theories or shattered your illusions with a few home truths. We shall probably never know.

Indeed, I like to think that I have defined for you the attitudes and beliefs so dear to we country dwellers, by illustrating the richly textured pageant of our heritage.

But what of the future? Well, as I sit here in my low-allergen garden, lulled by the computer-contolled gush of my water feature, sipping a soothing goblet of Elderflower Petillante, and only occasionally reaching for a paper hanky, I reflect on my up-coming aims and objectives for Ambridge. Yes, I have a dream – a Green dream actually – where a few simple aspirations might come to pass.

1. Borchester Environment Trust will help me sort out the confusion over Aethelwold's/Alf's hedge and apply for an SSSI, thus discouraging any further interest from the Grundy's.

2. Jean-Paul will captain the Ambridge Bulls in a friendly against the next deputation from Meyruelle, heroically overcoming his irrational Cathar prejudice, and laying to rest the thwarted spirit of Tante Mireille.

3. The once vocally challenged Mr Pullen, having already exhausted his limited English vocabulary and desperately seeking alien adjectives, will institute a 13-week French correspondence course, monitored by Aurore, entitled 'Franglais for the Few', to be held at the Village Hall, at a charge of 150 ecus, (approx. £25 – one hopes), concessions available.

4. Susan Carter will finally submit over the tedious matter of her neo-Georgian front door and agree to conceal it behind a quaintly thatched, rose-covered porch.

5. Ambridge will qualify for a cottage industry project grant under EU directive 2001 (Biotwine) 19/51/z50, to produce a fully organic, biodegradable, animal-orientated, non-toxic, farmer-friendly, Green baler twine.

And finally a personal dream – a to-be-fulfilled ambition if you will – to be voted Chairperson of the Parish Council and Producer in Residence of the Ambridge Players – unanimously!

So there you have it – my master plan to retain the Green scenario of Ambridge life into the next century. Call it my '2020 Vision'!